Workshop Drawing

Tubal Cain

SPECIAL INTEREST MODEL BOOKS

Special Interest Model Books Ltd.
Stanley House
3 Fleets Lane
Poole
Dorset
BH15 3AJ

First published by Argus Books Ltd. 1988
This 2nd edition published by Special Interest Model Books Ltd., 2003

ISBN 1-85486-182-4

Printed and bound in Great Britain by Cromwell Press Ltd., Trowbridge, Wilts.

Other books by the same author

Building Simple Model Steam
Engines
Building Simple Model Steam
Engines Book 2
Drills, Taps and Dies
Hardening, Tempering and
Heat Treatment
Milling Operations in the Lathe
The Model Engineer's
Handbook
Simple Workshop Devices
Soldering and Brazing
Spring Design and
Manufacture
Workholding in the Lathe

Writing as T.D. Walshaw

The I.S.O. System of Units
Ornamental Turning

Contents

Foreword

To offer one more book on engineering drawing when so many are available already may seem to be imprudent. However, it is an unfortunate fact, so far as the model engineer and amateur machinist is concerned, that almost all the existing books are either directed to the passing of examinations or intended to be used in conjunction with class teaching, or both. As a result the reader is faced with much matter which does not apply to workshop use and, at the same time, finds many gaps. This is inevitable, for to 'meet the syllabus' much theory must be covered and the class teacher of course, fills in the gaps. I know of only one book which could enable a raw beginner to learn to make (and hence to read) drawings from a clean sheet of paper* and that, unfortunately, seems to be out of print and, in any case, is based entirely on American practice.

In writing this book I have had in mind just those problems. I have tried to eliminate the academic theory, and to concentrate on the essentials needed to make good drawings. However, I must emphasise two things. First, engineering drawing is a highly *disciplined* subject. If complex machine parts are to be represented accurately on flat sheets of paper the rules must be observed; the conventions and the grammar' are both vital, and you will ignore them at your peril.

Secondly, in order to learn to *read* drawings it is necessary to know how they are made, and to know that you must make them yourself. So, right though the book, *practise as you read*. Don't leave it until later. I would emphasise, too, that 'mere sketching' is not to be disdained. Indeed, if pressed, I would assert that the ability to make a good sketch is more important than the making of a good drawing. There is really, no such thing as a 'mere' sketch! In fact, you will find that some of the illustrations in this book are sketches - two straight from the bench!

I have followed the current British Standard No 308 *Drawing Office Practice* throughout, but have retained some aspects of the earlier standards that are still acceptable, and which are easier both to follow and to execute than those currently 'preferred'. There is a world of difference in this respect between the needs of the industrial production department and those of the model engineer and jobbing machinist. I have included examples in both metric and imperial conventions of dimensioning, although most of the 'rules' on this aspect apply to either system.

I hope that you will find the book useful; and, even more, that you may come actually to enjoy making drawings. It is a very satisfying occupation.

Technical Drawing by Giesecke, Mitchell & Spencer (New York, Macmillan 1944)

Tubal Cain.
Longsleddale, Westmorland.

Introduction

It is perhaps significant that the use of 'drawings' for communication preceded the development of 'writing' by tens of thousands of years. This is not really that surprising, as a single sketch can convey data that might need hundreds of words - **Fig.1**. Furthermore, a well-executed drawing is far more *precise* than words; try describing a 3-throw crankshaft in *words alone* with sufficient detail to enable it to be manufactured. The use of drawing for such technical matters is at least 4,000 years old, though chiefly used in those days for architectural constructions and, perhaps, shipbuilding. A very significant fact about such drawings, which have survived from hose early days, is that they can readily be understood - even though, in some cases, the associated written language has yet to be deciphered.

Technical drawing, as we understand it is, however, of relatively recent date, and the type of drawing we use today very recent indeed. **Fig.2** shows a working drawing by Agricola *(1556)* describing the manufacture of a large bellows for supplying air to a smelting furnace. You will see that it is entirely pictorial in character. The complete bellows is shown at the bottom, and its components are spread over the rest of the sheet. (The original drawing would have been about 10 x 16

Fig.1 *How James Nasmyth ordered dinner at a Swedish inn in 1842 (Smiles' "Life of Nasmyth")*

7

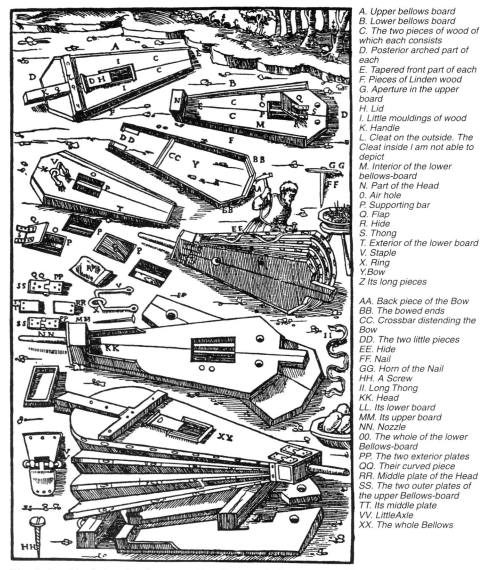

A. Upper bellows board
B. Lower bellows board
C. The two pieces of wood of which each consists
D. Posterior arched part of each
E. Tapered front part of each
F. Pieces of Linden wood
G. Aperture in the upper board
H. Lid
I. Little mouldings of wood
K. Handle
L. Cleat on the outside. The Cleat inside I am not able to depict
M. Interior of the lower bellows-board
N. Part of the Head
0. Air hole
P. Supporting bar
Q. Flap
R. Hide
S. Thong
T. Exterior of the lower board
V. Staple
X. Ring
Y. Bow
Z Its long pieces

AA. Back piece of the Bow
BB. The bowed ends
CC. Crossbar distending the Bow
DD. The two little pieces
EE. Hide
FF. Nail
GG. Horn of the Nail
HH. A Screw
II. Long Thong
KK. Head
LL. Its lower board
MM. Its upper board
NN. Nozzle
00. The whole of the lower Bellows-board
PP. The two exterior plates
QQ. Their curved piece
RR. Middle plate of the Head
SS. The two outer plates of the upper Bellows-board
TT. Its middle plate
VV. LittleAxle
XX. The whole Bellows

Fig. 2 *"working" drawing for a smelting furnace bellows, 1556. Though not all to the same scale the parts are all in proportion. Leading dimmensions were given in text.*

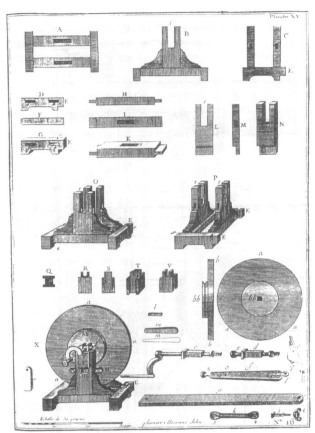

Fig.3 *Working drawing of a grindstone, 1748. The parts are to uniform scale, shown at the bottom. Both oblique and "orthographic" systems have been used. (Plumier - "L'Art de Tourner")*

inches tall.) There are no dimensions nor any attempt at a common scale - see the nail at FF, just above the workman, and the basket of nails just below. However, each view is in proportion and the actual dimensions of some parts are given in the text of the book *(De Re Metallica)* so that the craftsmen of the time would have no difficulty in building such a device. I quote an example where the width of the bellows is given as "3 feet. 2 palms and 3 digits wide" - units which were then as precise as our metres and millimetres.

Fig.3 is taken from L'Abbe Plumier's book on turning lathes, dated about 1749. It shows the parts and assembly of a

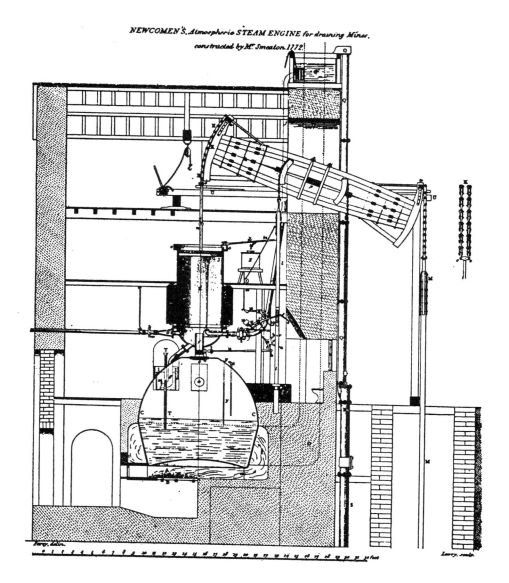

Fig.4 *An early drawing from "the age of steam". Note the scale. (Farey - "A Treatise on the Steam Engine, 1827")*

grindstone. Pictorial representation is still used, but the important parts are all shown *both* pictorially and in orthographic ('true drawing') views. All parts are to the same scale, and there is a scale of 'pouees' - French 'inches' - at the foot of the drawing. Again, there is further detail in the text of the book. (Incidentally, this explains the apparently redundant detail in the lower right-hand corner an addition to allow the wheel to be worked by treadle.)

It is important to understand how a craftsman making the devices worked in those days and, indeed, right up to the 12th century. He would most certainly not use the book, or a drawing, in the workshop, still less in the forest as seen in **Fig. 2**. If just one bellows or grindstone was required he would note the major dimensions, possibly scribe an outline on a piece of board for each part, and make each to fit. If the bellows was the odd digit larger or smaller this did not matter provided all the rest was in tune. If more than one object was required (e.g. wheelbarrows as shown in another of Agricola' s drawings) he would make one first and check that it served its office. This would then be taken to pieces and each part of this prototype would be used as a pattern so that all future barrows would be almost identical. Hence the origin of the use of the word 'off' to denote quantity. 'Three off' meant make three parts taken off that pattern or template.

It was not until the development of the steam engine that what we should recognise as engineering drawings made their appearance. **Fig. 4** is a drawing by Fary (1827) of one of Smeaton's Newcomen-type engines (1772) which is typical of these early days. It needed the invention of the *blue print* process in 1840 to allow copies of drawings to be distributed so that all the craftsmen concerned could work to identical drawings. Engineering drawings then became a truly international language, and it is now possible for workmen in any part of the world to be supplied with the same detail drawing.

Section 1

The Rules and 'Grammar' of Drawing

It has been fashionable for some time to believe that grammar does not matter so long as the meaning is clear. Fair enough so far as it goes, but that is not very far. A missing comma can sink a ship, and there is a great deal of difference between "no-one shall save me, I will drown" and "no-one will save me, I shall drown"; life and death, in fact. Loose constructions and punctuation in the written and spoken word can result in loss of clarity, but in the drawing office - or even on the sketch-pad -loose construction or careless presentation *always* leads to misunderstanding, sometimes fatal. This being so, I make no excuses for spending a considerable part of this book on the rules.

Lines

Drawings are, of course, made up of lines, and whether they be made with pencil, drawing pen, or even a window marker there are rules about which sort the draughtsman is to use for each purpose. The actual thickness used is determined by the type of drawing; one which is traced for reproduction as a white print will need thicker lines than, say, a design drawing where the degree of accuracy required dictates very thin lines. (I will deal with these various types later.) However, on the same drawing the general rule should be followed that (a) all lines should be *dense* which means using draughtsman's pencils, not those made for artists and (b) *thick* lines should be made from two to three times as wide as *thin* ones. When working in pencil the draughtsman achieves this by using a different *grade* of pencil, not by using a blunt one.

Fig. 5 shows the conventional use of the various types of line. The explanations are fairly clear, but a few notes may help. (**A**) is for the main outline, but also includes any edges which can be seen on the object. (**C**) refers to details within the object which cannot be seen e.g. a hole. I confess that my own practice is to make such lines a little thicker than thin. Good practice is to make the dashes twice the length of the spaces. (**D**) is, perhaps the most important line on the drawing in one respect, as it is very often the line from which dimensions are measured. Such lines should always be really sharp and, though thin, positive. The function of line (**E**) will appear in an example in a moment, and I shall be dealing

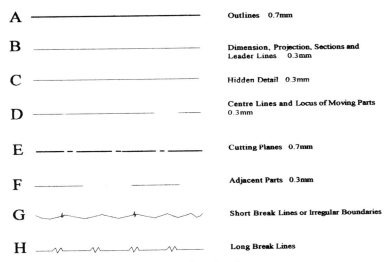

A	Outlines 0.7mm
B	Dimension, Projection, Sections and Leader Lines 0.3mm
C	Hidden Detail 0.3mm
D	Centre Lines and Locus of Moving Parts 0.3mm
E	Cutting Planes 0.7mm
F	Adjacent Parts 0.3mm
G	Short Break Lines or Irregular Boundaries
H	Long Break Lines

Fig.5 *Types of lines for use on engineering drawings*

with it in more detail later in the book. Current practice here is to use a thin line with thick ends for this purpose **(Fig.6)** but the full thick line should be used if there is risk of any confusion. (**F**) seldom arises in

Fig.6 *Alternative method for indicating cutting planes. See text.*

run-of-the-mill drawing, but when used it is important that the *length* of the dashes should be markedly less than those used for centrelines, (**D**), (**G**) and (**H**) are used to indicate that the whole of the object has not been drawn. In the case of long, round shafts the convention shown in **Fig. 7** is used when details of the two ends are

drawn but the centre part is not drawn. **Fig. 8** is a drawing of a 'something' showing the application of the various types of line.

An important rule. Where centrelines cross they should always intersect on part

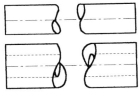

Fig.7 *Break lines for circular parts, solid or hollow.*

of the long dash. You will see on **Fig. 8** that at the lower boss of the lever and at the centre of the upper hole on the right. is not the case. *This is wrong.*

Letters and figures

We may need to add notes to drawings and in almost all cases there must be

13

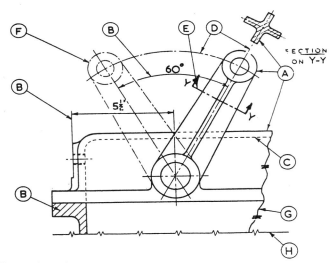

Fig.8 *An illustration of the use of the various types of line (After BS308-1953)*

dimensions. There is no rut as to style - anything that is legible will do so far as lettering is concerned. In the old days the lettering on drawings was a real example of the calligrapher's art, but we have neither the time nor the skill to follow their example. Plain block capitals are safest, vertical or sloping at about 20 degrees, but all should be one or the other. Many amateurs tend to use *lettering stencils.* If you expect to do much drawing it is far better to spend just a little time practising freehand. Stencils are very slow, are costly (and need special pens or pencils) and, worst of all, take all the character out of the drawing. However, clarity is the essential, and if your hand-letter is so bad that others cannot read it, buy some stencils. **Fig. 9** shows some clear and bold styles, but avoid the broad type of letter except perhaps for titles, as it takes up too much room than necessary. I also show my own freehand styles not as a pattern, but to show the difference between stencil

and personal characters. Figures are even more important. It is always possible to decipher badly formed words from the context, but a single obscure figure can be disastrous. **Fig. 10** shows acceptable styles, but the "1" having a sloping serif at the top is discouraged for fear it might be confused with "7". On the continent the latter is written with a bar, $\mathcal{7}$, to make sure. The use of a computer zero is *not* acceptable, as it can be confused with a Greek symbol. I have shown my own style of figures as well.

Important rules for figures

(1) The bar in fractions must always be horizontal i.e. $\frac{3}{4}$ *never* 3/4.

(2) Decimal fractions less than zero should always be preceded by "0", thus 0.375, *never* .375.

(3) A comma or a space should be set between every three numerals where there are more than four, thus 11,234 or 11 234.

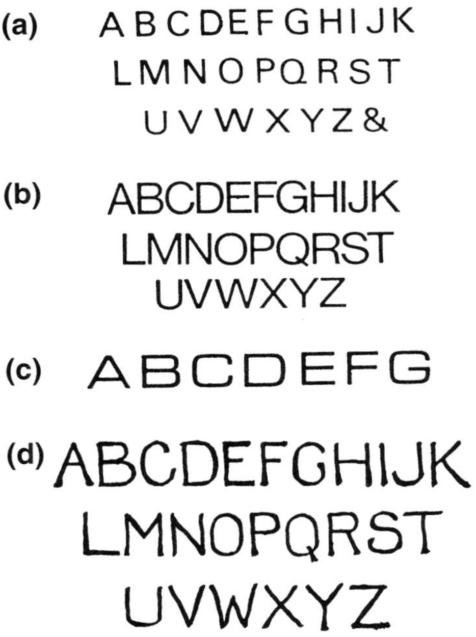

(a) A B C D E F G H I J K
L M N O P Q R S T
U V W X Y Z &

(b) ABCDEFGHIJK
LMNOPQRST
UVWXYZ

(c) A B C D E F G

(d) ABCDEFGHIJK
LMNOPQRST
UVWXYZ

Fig.9a & b *Acceptable letter-forms for use on drawings.*
(c) This broader form of lettering should only be used for titles.
(d) "Hand-done" lettering can add character and is often quicker than using stencils

this is *downright wrong.* Rule (2) causes no hardship and avoids the risk of (e.g.) .008 being read as 0.08. The spacing of numerals in threes makes both for clarity and for ease of recollection.

We shall be returning to the use of numerals later, when we come to consider the *dimensioning* of drawings. We shall also be looking at some other conventions - rules - about the representation of the more common machine parts like screw threads and so on. But it is time to deal with the most important convention of all and that needs a new chapter. Read on.

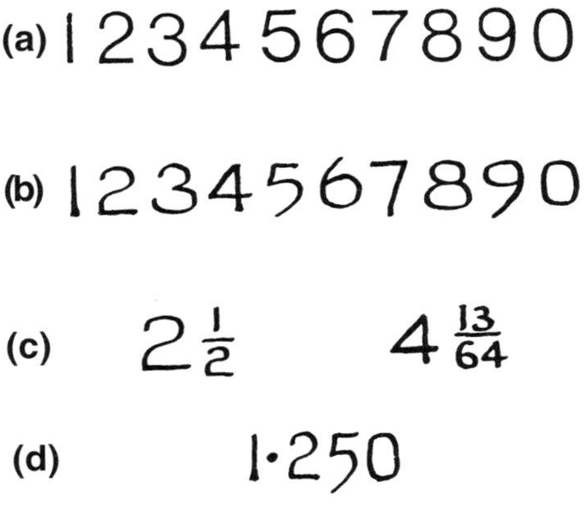

(a) 1 2 3 4 5 6 7 8 9 0

(b) 1 2 3 4 5 6 7 8 9 0

(c) $2\frac{1}{2}$ $4\frac{13}{64}$

(d) 1·250

Fig. 10a *Acceptable forms of numerals for dimensioning.*
(b) "Hand-done" figures are often preferable to the use of stencils, as this example shows.
(c) The fractions should stand above and below the height of primary numerals. The fraction is abour 25% taller.
(d) Decimal points should be bold and given adequate space.

The space is preferred as some continental countries use the comma as a decimal point. But note that no space is needed with four digits - 1124 is correct, not 1 124.

The reasons for these rules are clear. If carelessly written, 13/32 could be read as 1 $3/32$. I doubt if there is any engineering works in the country (or joiner's shop for that matter) which has not had this experience. It is unfortunate that the use of stencils for lettering means that lazy people tend to use the oblique stroke, but

Section 2

The Conventions of 'Projection'

Projection is the means used to show the drawn object from different directions. In some cases a single view would be sufficient. It may look the same from all directions - a ball or a cube - or we may be able to deduce the other view. In **Fig. 11** for example, the end view is clearly two concentric circles and it would be a waste of space to draw it. For the majority of objects, however, this is not possible, and we must look

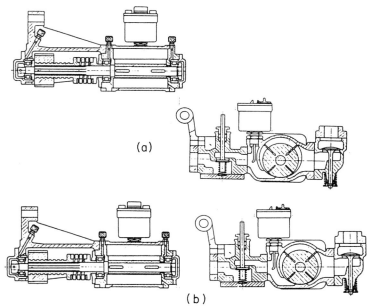

(a)

(b)

Fig. 12 *Both (a) and (b) are accurate as drawings, but (b) is easier to read.*

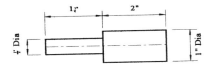

Fig. 11 *No end view is necessary as the part is clearly circular in shape.*

at it from several sides and draw what we see. **Fig. 12** shows, at the top (a) two sectional views of a compressed air motor, one along the spindle, the other at right angles.

They are accurate and clear, but not so easy to follow as the identical views rearranged as shown below, at (b). These are *in projection,* on the same centreline; much easier to read and, in fact, to draw.

It is very unfortunate that if you enrol for a drawing class you will almost certainly be introduced to this aspect of drawing via a tedious and rather academic route, dealing with abstruse geometrical shapes which appear to have little relevance to real engineering. Yet it is really quite straightforward.

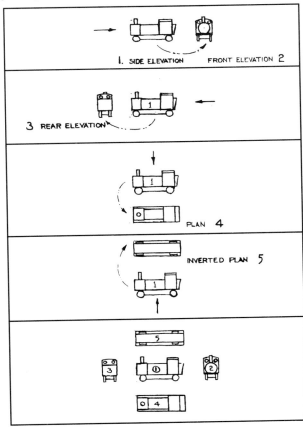

Fig. 13 *Illustrating "English" or "First Angle" projection.*

Look at **Fig.13**. Here I am making a rough (very rough) sketch of a small toy locomotive. To draw the side elevation at (1) I have placed the loco in front of me and drawn what I saw. To obtain the view of the smoke-box front elevation (which some would call the end elevation) I turn the toy through 90 degrees and again draw what I see at (2). This is the same view that I would have seen had the loco backed round a 90-degree curve, and it is in the same relative position. In turning the toy round to see the

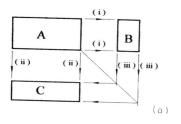

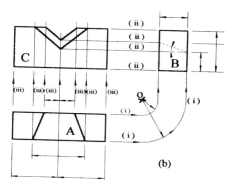

Fig. 14 *Steps in deriving views by "pure" projection methods. Note the alternative methods of taking projection lines "round a corner".*

front it would tend to move to the right.

To get a view of the bunker end (3), we do exactly the same thing, turning the object through 90 degrees; this time the loco has shunted *forwards* round the bend, so the view appears on the left of the main elevation. Again, to obtain the plan view, looking down on the boiler top (4) we turn the loco towards us through 90 degrees, and to obtain the underside view (5) we turn it the opposite way, so that the view appears above the initial position. If we now assemble all these views onto one sheet of paper, each in the same relative position to the main view (1), we get the relationship seen at the bottom of **Fig. 13.** *It is the relative position of these views which is important,* as the position of the view defines the face we are looking at. Not, perhaps, very important when making a drawing of a familiar object like this one, but if the drawing were of the full-size loco's inside cylinders it would be **vital**.

This method of projection is known as Natural, First Angle or English projection. Natural because it is the way children instinctively draw things; First angle, because the object is turned through 90 degrees, one right angle; and English because this distinguishes it from a different system originating in the USA about 1870 and which became the American standard in 1935. (I deal with the theoretical derivation of both systems in the appendix at the end of the book.). The use of projection not only assists the interpretation of a drawing, it makes it much easier to *prepare* the drawing in the first place. Look at **Fig. 14**. At **(a)** we have a simple solid - say a matchbox. We first draw the Front Elevation, A, by measurement. To draw the end elevation of face B we *project* the two lines marked

(i) to determine the height, and measure the width only. To obtain the plan view C, we need not *measure* anything, as the position of the lines can be obtained by projecting from the other two views. To turn these projection lines round the corner I have used a diagonal reference line, set at 45 degrees, as you see. Try this for yourself - but *do it now* Try *every* example in the book as you read it, you will find it much easier to follow that way.

At **Fig. 14b** is a slightly more complicated object. I have shown dimension lines to indicate the dimensions we know and can measure. In this case the Plan view is drawn first, and I have shown an alternative method of taking the projection lines round the corner. Try it for yourself, and draw the front elevation. Remember **Fig. 13**; keep visualising the turning of the object through 90 degrees to get a view of the face to be drawn.

Plans - a digression

The habit seems to have grown of calling *any* drawing a Plan; indeed, there is an official Plans Service However, in the grammar of engineering drawing a Plan is specifically the view from above. The Plans Service provides Drawings or Prints, and I *very strongly* advise you to refer to them as such. If you write to any chief draughtsman for the plans of a machine you may not get what you want.

American or third angle projection

In this case the object is imagined to be set within a glass box and the outline drawn on the outside of the glass. If this box is then opened out the views appear as in **Fig. 15**. Compare this with **Fig. 13**. You will observe that the plan is now above the front elevation instead of below, and that the two end elevations are reversed.

Fig. 16 is a simpler comparison between the two systems. The method of deriving one view from another by projection lines is exactly the same in both cases; the difference lies in the relative position of the views.

Which is correct? The answer is that either will do, provided that the type of projection used is *clearly* indicated on the drawing. Although you can use either, you most certainly should *not* use both on the same drawing or, worse still, draw one view of an object in one style and another in the other; the quickest way of getting the sack in any drawing office.

Since writing this part I have come across several published drawings which commit just this crime. One is of a rather complex cylinder block. Five views are given, one in section. This section and the end view are in third angle. The plan, set directly below the elevation, is in first angle and the rear elevation is set out of projection but with no direction arrows to show the face it represents. I can read it - but

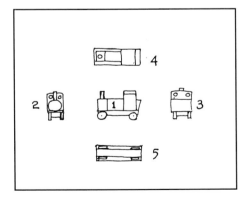

Fig. 15 *The toy loco of Fig. 13 drawn in "American" or "Third Angle" projection.*

19

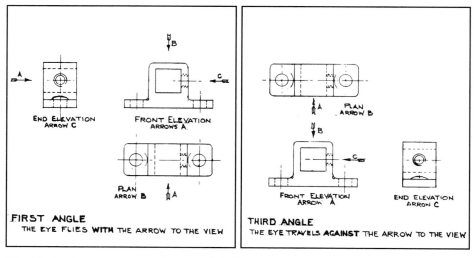

Fig. 16 *Another comparison between "First" and "Third Angle" projection. The lettered arrows point to the same faces in both cases.*

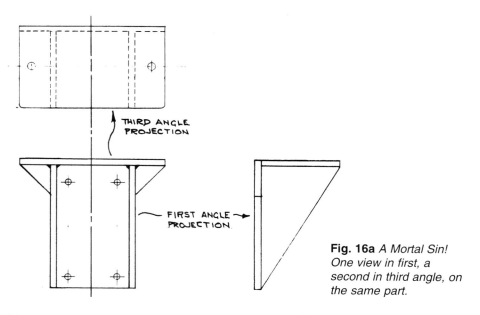

Fig. 16a *A Mortal Sin! One view in first, a second in third angle, on the same part.*

20

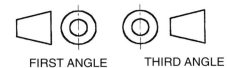

FIRST ANGLE   THIRD ANGLE

Fig. 17 *The international symbol indicating the projection system. This should appear on ALL drawings.*

then, I have had 70 years' experience of reading drawings, many very complex indeed. But such an arrangement is just not fair on the less experienced.

The second example I have copied in **Fig. 16A**, but have left out the dimensions. This one may present no problems in reading, but there is no reason at all why the three views should not have been set in correct projection - either first or third angle.

My own practice is to use natural or first angle projection throughout, subject only to the exceptions which apply to any rule and which I deal with shortly. I have listened to argument on the merits of each style for over 60 years now. Each has its valid merits and both have their disadvantages. These balance each other so finely that neither can be labelled right or wrong and both are accepted by International Standards Institutions. But as I was making drawings of things as a child for a good ten years before I was 'taught' to draw I found the first angle system almost instinctive and always use it. (Note how the eye tends to follow the arrows in the left-hand sketch at **(a), Fig. 16**.) I always recommend the use of first angle by amateur draughtsmen.

However, *you MUST indicate on every drawing which system is used*. This should be done in words in one corner of the draw-ing *and* by the use of the international symbols shown in **Fig. 17**. This is absolutely vital, and more so nowadays when drawings are travelling internationally. Don't forget and if 'Plans' send you a drawing without this indication, write and tell them about it

Exceptions

It is the mark of a good draughtsman that the drawing be well arranged, with neither crowding nor with blank spaces wasting expensive paper. This means that quite frequently a strict adherence to the rules of either system of projection cannot be followed. For example, both **Fig. 13** and **Fig. 15** waste a lot of space. It is quite legitimate to rearrange the views as I have shown in **Fig. 18**. The rearrangement makes for a much clearer drawing and provided that the view indicators A and B are bold there is no risk of confusion. The only disadvantage is that we can no longer project one view from another. This sys-

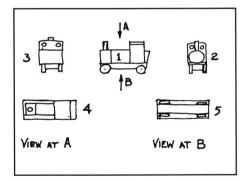

Fig. 18 *If some views are not in strict "projection" the direction of view should be shown by lettered arrows. This can save space compared with Fig. 13.*

tem is particularly useful when we need to show the *section* of an object, a matter dealt with later.

A second, and possibly obvious exception is when an object is so large that views must be spread over two or more drawings. In such a case the view indicators should also carry the drawing number on which the view will appear.

An interesting example

I have included **Fig. 19** just to show you what can be done with very simple projection methods. The object is to produce a set of three true views of a matchbox standing on one of its corners. The procedure is shown on the drawing; we start at I with the normal upright position. At II we have tilted it on the lower edges, the front elevation (A) retaining the true lengths of. At III we have taken the plan view of II and turned it through an angle, and derived the other views from it. Finally, at IV the end elevation of has been cocked over at an angle and the other views projected from it as described in the caption. Try it for yourself - even freehand sketching with a suitable box to look at and see how you get on. Incidentally, don't be alarmed if some of the views seem to turn themselves inside out now and then. This is a not uncommon optical illusion inherent in these oblique views

Other forms of representation

The projections we have looked at are what is known as *orthographic.* That means that if, for example, a cube is drawn the face will show all lines at their true length and all angles at their true value. However, we can see only one face at a time, and for some people the use of several views does

seem to make it difficult for them to *visualise* the overall shape of the object. We can, of course, revert to the artistic pictorial representation (see in **Fig. 2** for example) but this needs some skill as an artist, not given to many of us. Some geometrically valid form of pictorial representation had to be found.

The oldest form of these is, perhaps, the use of *perspective.* This approximates very nearly to the eye's view of the object, and assumes that all lengths set down on the drawing are proportional to their distance from imaginary vanishing points at the implied horizon. Contrary to supposition, it is possible for such representations to be scaled from - indeed, they must be scaled TO to make the drawing - but it is difficult and *very* time-consuming. For this reason true perspective drawings are used, in engineering examples, only for display purposes, possibly in sales literature.

In *isometric* projection, three of the faces can be seen on the one view. To enable lengths to be truly scaled the object must be angled so that the lengths of all edges of an ideal cube still appear to be the same length. See **Fig. 20**. The cube has been rotated on its vertical axis through 45 degrees, and at the same time tilted forward through an angle of 35 degrees 15 seconds. The measured lengths of each side are the same, and will be 0.8165 (square root of 2/3) of their true lengths. The angles XOY, XOZ and YOZ which are 90 degrees on the actual cube appear as exactly 120 degrees on the drawing. With this type of representation, of course, all circles will appear as ellipses as seen at (b) in **Fig. 20**. (This applies to all oblique or pictorial types of view.) While isometric views were, at one time, always drawn with

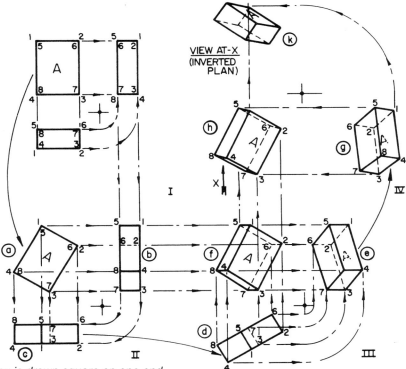

VIEW AT-X
(INVERTED PLAN)

1. Box is drawn square on one end.

2. Box tilted on one end 3-7. "a" ia all true dimension. In "b" width only is true. Draw "a" first, set off true width in "b" and project from "a" for foreshortened lengths. "c" is completed by projection from "a" and "b".

3. Box now turned through 30 deg. still on edge 3-7. Draw "d" from view "c" as this is still of the same dimensions. Project heights from "a" to "f" and widths from "d". Complete "e" by projection from "f" and "d".

4. Box turned on corner 3. "g" is dimensionally similar to "e" but tilted to right. Draw "g" from "e" by measurement. Project "h" from "g" and "f", "k" from "g" and "h". (Note - "k" is inverted plan).

Fig. 19 *An exercise in projection. The view at 4 is obtained from that at 1 with the minimum of measurement.*

scales which allowed for the ratio mentioned above it is now common practice to draw the view using 'true lengths'; this simply makes the drawing 22 per cent larger. The system is not used a great deal these days, as it looks all wrong and is slow in execution.

Isometric has now been replaced by the *trimetric* system. This involves arranging the three planes of the ideal cube to be

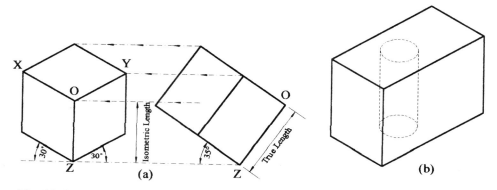

Fig. 20 *A pictorial view, using the system of 'isometric' projection.*

tilted by *different* angles, such that the scale lengths in the three planes are in a convenient ratio e.g. ¼, 1/5 and 1/6. The resulting view of the object is then much more acceptable, and, in addition, by allotting the larger of these scales to one or other of the edges of the cube the view can be adjusted to suit the nature of the object being drawn. **Fig. 21** shows a machine base. At the top is the ordinary engineering drawing as would be used in the shop. Below are three trimetric views, allotting the scales

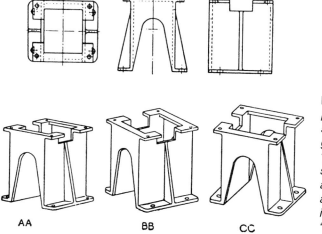

AA   BB   CC

Fig. 21 *"Trimetric" projection, using a special square (Fig. 23), gives a more natural "pictorial" effect. The system can provide alternative viewpoints, as shown. (From the instruction book to the "Trimetric Square").*

24

Fig. 22 *A further example of "trimetric" projection. (Engineering)*

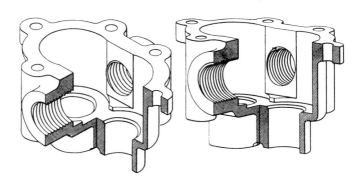

differently each time. **Fig. 22** is another example, showing how a change in scale ratio can clarify the view of the internal parts. It might be thought that such a drawing is very difficult to make, and so it can be. However, about 60 years ago Messrs Metropolitan Vickers patented a Trimetric Scale (sadly no longer available) which greatly facilitates the projection (see **Fig. 23**) and with this the making of a trimetric

Fig. 23 *The combined trimetric square and scales, as patented by The Metropolitan-Vickers Company in 1937.*

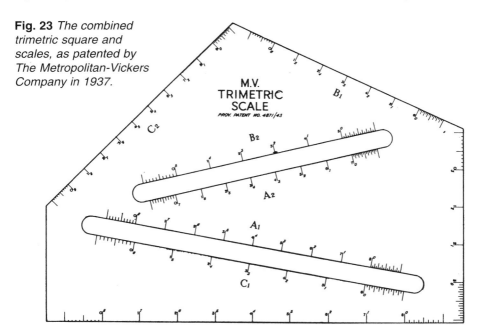

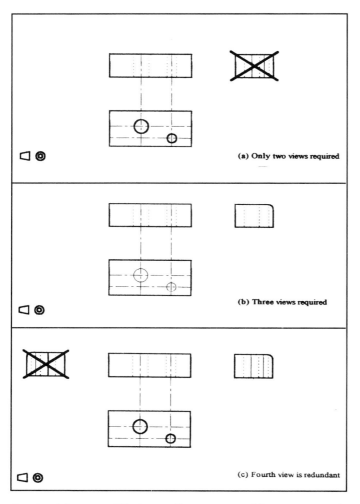

Fig. 24 *Examples of "required" and "redundant" views.*

(a) Only two views required

(b) Three views required

(c) Fourth view is redundant

drawing takes very little longer than an ordinary one. True, constructing the ellipses takes time, but, on the other hand, there is only one view to draw. However, its main use is as a 'pictorial' to help workers, in the pattern shop especially, to visualise the *shape* of the object to be made.

How many views?

We have just remarked that an oblique projection of any sort can show in one view information which may take three or more in normal orthographic representation. This immediately raises the question "How many views are necessary in the normal engi-

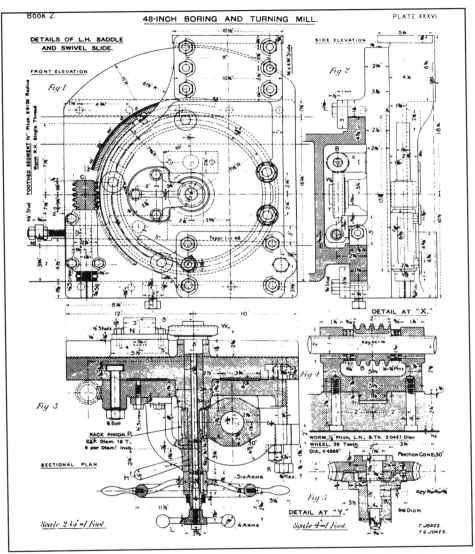

Fig. 25 *An example of the type of drawing used in workshops in the 1880's. Even then, separate drawings of individual parts were preferred. ("Machine Drawing" - Jones & Jones, 1907)*

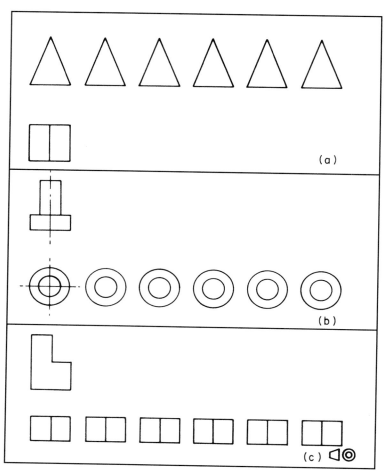

(a)

(b)

(c)

neering drawing?". There can be no rule. There must be enough views to ensure that there is no risk of misinterpretation. In **Fig. 24** two views at (a) should suffice, but three are needed at (b). On the other hand, the additional view at (c) is redundant; it conveys no additional information, and wastes space. However, on a complex object it may be necessary to add such redundant views because otherwise the number of dimensions on the necessary ones may be overcrowded and it can be said that too many views are better than too few. **Fig. 25** is such an example, in the style of drawing commonly used about 100 years ago. There is sufficient information to allow all the parts to be made, but the risk of confusion is considerable. Today, of course, each part would be laid out on a separate drawing, with an 'arrangement' drawing for the erectors. At the other extreme, **Fig. 26** is an exercise given to students in a drawing class: (b) and (c) are plan views and (a) a row of elevations. Each has one example of the elevations. Make a sketch and see how many different objects these could represent (some students found more than six). **Fig. 26A** is a case where a third view is not essential, but might be helpful. As we shall see later, in many cases a partial view, of just one aspect of the object, may ease visualisation as well as simplify the dimensioning. It is not a bad idea either when dealing with a component which is an unusual shape to set a thumbnail sketch in one corner of the drawing to give a pictorial view. **Fig. 27** is an example; the parts

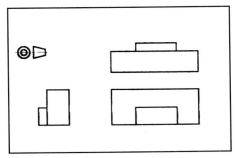

Fig. 26a *A case where two views are sufficient but a third might help to interpret the shape.*

of the fabrication were fully detailed, but this sketch (in trimetric) helps to show the shape as well as clarifying the order of assembly.

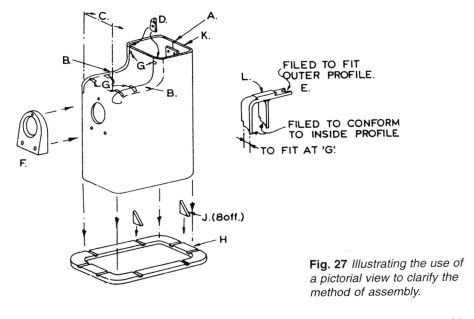

Fig. 27 *Illustrating the use of a pictorial view to clarify the method of assembly.*

Section 3

What Lies Inside the Object?

Hidden Details and Sections

It is the rule rather than the exception that engineering components are literally 'holes surrounded by metal' and the shape of these holes is vital to the operation of the machine. We need a means of describing and dimensioning these holes. There are two methods; one is to show the hidden detail, using dotted lines (see **Fig. 5**) to distinguish between this and the outline and the other is to draw a sectional view, again using some convention of lines to indicate the fact. Let us deal with these in turn.

Hidden details

The first rule *is that the main views should be chosen so that the minimum of hidden detail drawing is needed.* Thus a part which is hollow at the back might be drawn with a rear elevation instead of the usual front as the main view. A plethora of dotted lines on a drawing can be very confusing. **Fig. 28** is a case in point; the detail of the square flange would be better shown by offering a partial view in the direction of the arrow (which I have added)

'X'. The other detail required was clear from the other views on the full drawing.

Whether dotted lines should be used to indicate the presence of hidden edges in one view which are clear in another is a debatable point. You are making the drawing for one purpose only - to convey information. If the addition of dotted lines in one view to show detail which is clear in another would make the drawing easier to follow, then they should be included. If such dotted lines will not clutter up the drawing and make it hard to read, then they may be included. But if the drawing is already full of detail, and especially if it carries many dimensions, it is best to omit hidden detail on that view, and, if need be, draw an extra one to show the detail.

Rules

(1) Where a dotted line *meets* a full line or another dotted line the 'dash' should touch - **Fig. 29** (a) to (c).

(2) Where a dotted line *crosses* a full line the latter should lie in the gap between dashes. But if two dotted lines cross, one should show a dash in the gaps on the other, **Fig. 29d.**

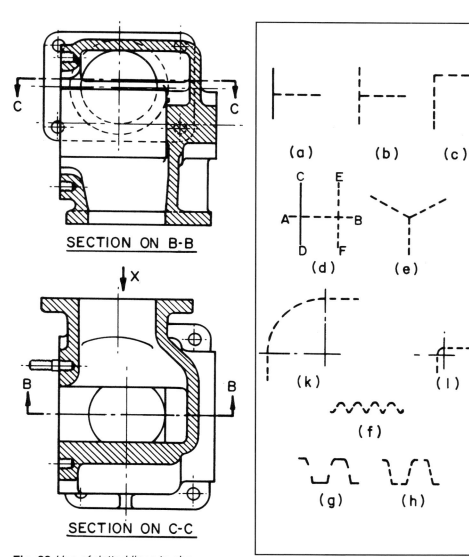

SECTION ON B-B

SECTION ON C-C

Fig. 28 *Use of dotted lines to show hidden detail In this case an extra view might be preferable , as explained in the text. (After BS308-1953)*

Fig. 29 *Illustrating the rules governing the use of dotted lines. The cases are discussed in the text.*

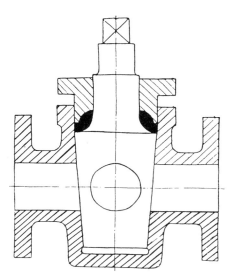

Fig. 30 *Use of section lines on adjacent parts. Solis black has been used for the packing; cross-hatching is preferred in this situation.*

(3) If three or more dotted lines meet at a point the meeting should be on dashes in each case, **Fig. 29e**.

(4) When drawing arcs in dotted lines the end of the curve should coincide with the end of a dash, **Fig. 29k** and (**l).**

Fig. 29f shows the treatment of screw threads in hidden detail, but this method of representation is now permitted rather than preferred. We shall be dealing with this matter later. Shown at (**g**) and (**h**) is the treatment of gear teeth in cases where the profile is shown complete, (**g**) is for small teeth, and (**h**) for large. For very large teeth there might be more dashes on the flanks, but there should always be a bent dash at the corners.

Drawing these dotted (really they are dashed) lines is not easy - there is a temptation to rush the job. The most common fault is excessive length of the dash with ragged ends. Try to keep a ratio of dash to space of between 2:1 and 3:1. As already noticed, current practice is to draw these lines thin, but I try to make them just a little more emphatic than centrelines, though not as bold as outlines.

Sectioned views

The sectioned view is by far the most effective way of showing the internal shape and dimension of an object - whether it be a complete engine or a small part. It is clear, and provided that the conventions are observed seldom prone to misinterpretation. The view imagines that the part has been cut or broken and shows the cut face, which is indicated by section lines or hatching, drawn (as a rule) at an angle of 45 degrees to the main axis of the drawing - **Fig. 30**. You will see that where two parts meet the section lines run in opposite directions. To get over the difficulty when *three* parts meet (as for the packing in the sketch) the draughtsman has used full black, but it would be more usual to use cross hatching here. Note that the section lines are thinner than the outline and regularly spaced - a most important matter.

Many find difficulty in achieving this, but it is quite easy. All you have to do is to scribe a line along each edge of your 45-degree set-square, 1.5mm from the edge on one, 2.5mm on another, and 3.5mm from the edge on the third. When you have drawn one section line, advance the square until the line lies below the scribed line on the square and draw another, and so on. As you may, occasionally, need section lines at 30 or 60 degrees rather than 45, do the same on your 60-degree square as well.

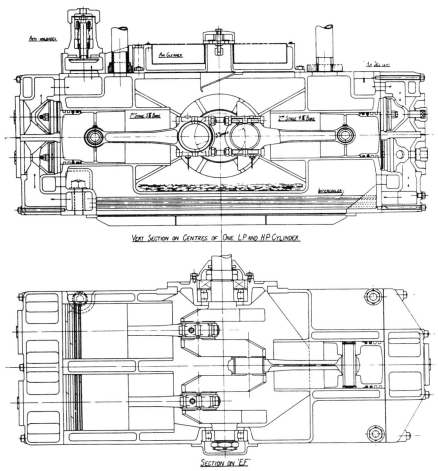

VERT SECTION ON CENTRES OF ONE LP AND HP CYLINDER

SECTION ON 'EF'

Fig. 31 *Cross-section of an air compressor designed by the author. Because the wall thicknesses are so small, section lines have not been used.*

Before going on to the conventions and rules governing sectional views, a word about one special case or, rather, practice. On many drawings you may find that there are *no section lines at all*. This is, in part, due to sheer laziness, but there is a problem when drawings have to be reduced considerably in size for reproduction in a magazine or book. The section lines may then come so close together that they appear as a blur, and to avoid this the draughtsman has left them off, **Fig. 31**. This is a pity, as it can cause confusion. The problem can be avoided either by drawing the section lines slightly farther apart or, better still, by asking the printer to lay on a tint, as I have done in **Fig. 32**. It does add slightly to the cost, but a drawing is such an important part of any constructional article that this is warranted.

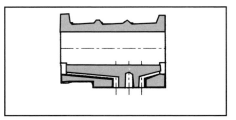

Fig. 32 *"Shading" using a tint, can be helpful on small parts.*

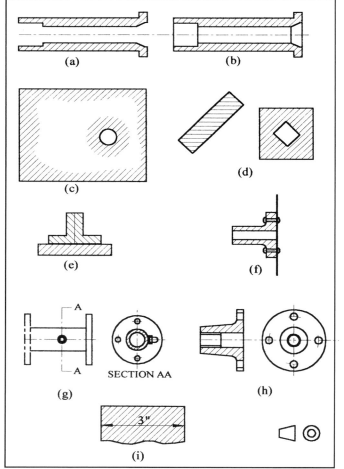

Fig. 33 *Some of the rules and conventions governing the use of sections. Note the example at (a) - a very bad mistake often made by the amateur. (b) is the correct representation as explained in the text.*

Fig. 33 shows a few of the conventions but starts at (**a**) with an all too common mistake. The section has been drawn, but the lines indicating the edges visible behind the cutting plane have been left off, so that the spindle appears to be in two pieces. The correct interpretation of such a section is seen at (**b**). Don't forget this point: *all* edges visible behind the cutting plane must be shown.

When large areas are to be sectioned, it is in order to draw section lines, hatching, around the edges only, as at (**c**). However, if there is any detail within the mass, say a hole, it must be hatched round, as indicated. If the hole or feature is small the lines may be closer together around it.

Clarity is all-important, and situations may arise where hatching at 45 degrees may cause confusion. Two cases are shown at (**d**), where the section lines are set to avoid running parallel to an edge.

We have already noted in passing that there can be a problem where two parts meet a third in section. The convention is shown at (**e**). Two parts are hatched at the same angle, but the lines are *staggered* where they meet - this is regarded as preferable to hatching one of them at a different angle. There are also difficulties with very thin sections. These are dealt with by using a thick black line instead of hatching, (**f**); the thickness need not be exactly to scale. It is, however, important that such a line be *solid black, as* otherwise it may be mistaken for the conventional representation of insulating material.

Indicating the position of the section plane is, of course, very important, especially on a complicated object. This is shown at (**g**), where a thin line runs through the boss, terminated by two thick arrows

Fig. 34 *Shafts, keys, webs and similar parts are never sectioned as there is no hidden detail to reveal.*

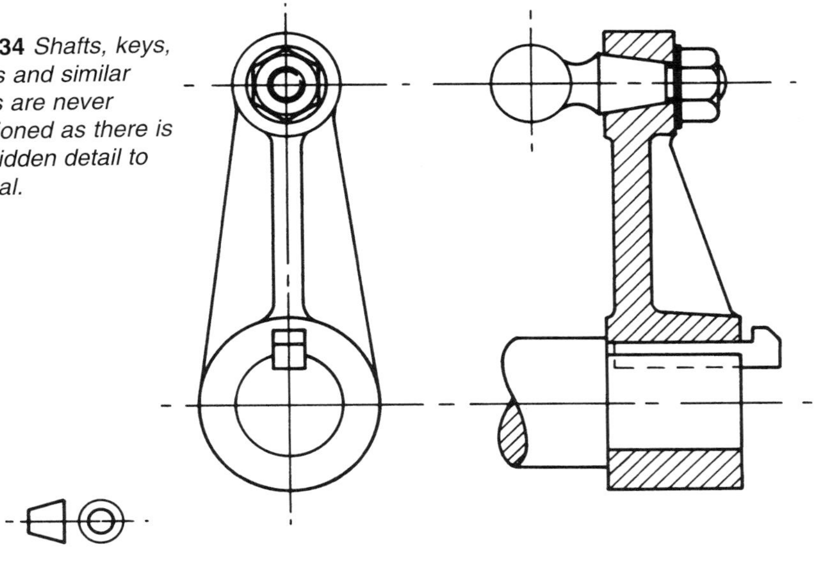

pointing towards the sectional view and lettered for identification. Note that the convention of projection — first or third angle - used on the rest of the drawing should be followed where possible, though the arrows will prevent any confusion. However, if the section is taken on a normal centreline, as at (**h**), then there is no need for any arrows provided the section is properly projected. Finally on this sheet I show at (**i**) how dimensions must be treated. The figures are set in a space in the hatching, but the dimension line runs over them.

Parts that are never sectioned

There is no point in sectioning a part that contains no hidden detail. For this reason shafts, keys, bolts, rivets, wheel spokes, and webs are *never* sectioned on their longways centreline. This is illustrated on **Fig. 34**. You will see that the parts I have mentioned are all unsectioned. In the case of the web, it is sometimes prudent to write the word WEB across it, especially when dealing with webs inside castings. The sectioning of these parts is the second most common error in amateur drawings. To do so is not only a waste of time and pencil

lead, but also makes the drawing much more difficult to interpret.

Fig. 35 illustrates yet another error. There is absolutely *no need* to show the hidden detail as on the left-hand view. The detail is *not,* in fact, hidden, as it can be deduced very simply from the outline of the wheel, as seen in the right-hand view. Dotted lines may be necessary on a sectioned view, of course, but they should only be used when necessary. The guiding rule is to include sufficient information for the part to be made, or the construction followed, yet to avoid cluttering the drawing with so much detail that it becomes confusing. Better to show a few more views than to smother one with hatching and dotted lines.

Other forms of sectional views

At **Fig. 36a** we have the half section. This is extremely useful for symmetrical objects, one half an outside view and the other sectioned. Note that there is no full line at the junction. At (**b**) is the partial section, which is self-explanatory; there is no point in sectioning the complete object in a case like this. **Fig. 36c** is a section on two planes. The cutting plane is indicated by the thin lines thickened at the change of direction and at the ends. In this case the alternative method of indicating direction is shown - the arrows point *to* the line, instead of forming part of it as on **Fig. 33g** and on **Fig. 36f**. Note that in this example one of the branches is in full section and the other in half section, and that a limited amount of hidden detail is shown to avoid the need to draw a further detail of the coring.

Revolved sections are shown at (**d**) and (**e**). For a relatively short piece the

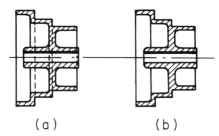

(a)   (b)

Fig. 35 *There is no need for the dotted lines at (a), as the apparently "missing" detail is evident from the outline. (b) is correct.*

Fig. 36 *Sectioning methods which save time and space.*

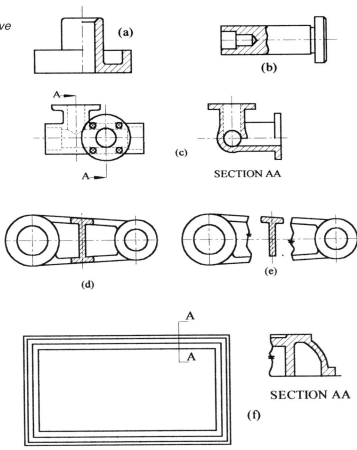

(a)

(b)

(c)

SECTION AA

(d)

(e)

SECTION AA

(f)

section is superimposed on the outline; note that these outlines run up to the sectional view but do not cross it. In the case of a longer object the revolved section can be shown detached, between the break lines as at (**e**). Finally, at (**f**) we have the removed or detached section, which in the view shown is also an enlarged section. The latter should always carry a note stating the degree of enlargement - in this case four times the scale of the main view of the object. In passing, note again the two methods of indicating the direction of view at the cutting plane shown at (**c**) and (**f**). The current preferred method is shown at (**c**) but either will do and I prefer (f) as being more positive - especially on assembly drawings having a number of sectional views.

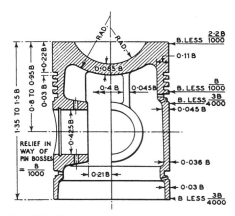

Fig. 36A *On symmetrical parts the sections on two axes can be drawn as one thus saving space. (from "Diesel Engine Design", T.D.Walshaw. Geo. Newnes, 1949)*

Fig. 36A illustrates a very compact way of showing sections of symmetrical parts. The left-hand half of the view shows a section along the axis of the gudgeon pin, while that right-hand half is a section at right angles. This method is much used for spare parts lists or, as in this case, to show the relative proportions of the parts ('B' is the cylinder bore on this drawing). It is seldom used for dimensioned drawings.

In **Fig. 37** we have the conventions for successive sections, where, for example, a shaft carries a number of different shapes on the diameter. The preferred method is to show the sections in true projection, as at the top of the sketch. However, this can be wasteful of space on the drawing, in which case the sections can be set below the elevation of the shaft. Again, the preferred convention is that each sectional view should have its centreline on the line of the cutting plane. However, if this is not possible e.g. due to cutting planes being too close together, the sectional views may be set at your convenience, provided that each is properly labelled.

Oblique sections (Fig. 38)

Sectional views are frequently useful in pictorial assembly drawings, of which this drawing is an example. Care must be taken

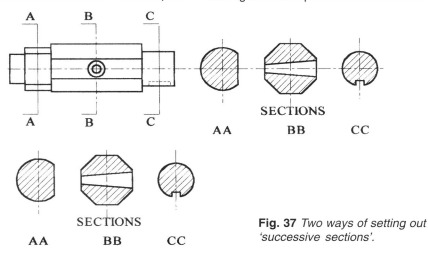

Fig. 37 *Two ways of setting out 'successive sections'.*

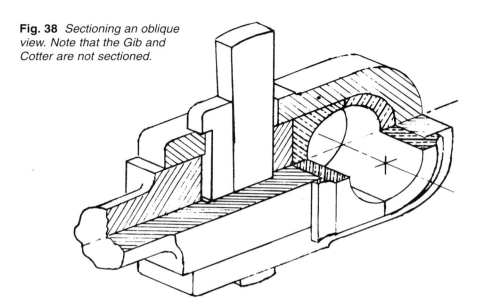

Fig. 38 *Sectioning an oblique view. Note that the Gib and Cotter are not sectioned.*

over the orientation of the section lines – hatching - if confusion is to be avoided. First, note that the cotters are not sectioned, and hence are shown projecting in front of the section planes. Then, note the more or less flat alignment of the hatching on the horizontal surface of the section. A very odd optical illusion results from reversing the run of the lines in the two planes. Using slightly bolder lines on the horizontal surface can enhance the effect. Finally, you will see that a different type of hatching has been used for the bearing brasses. This is now regarded as old-fashioned, and it certainly takes a bit longer to draw. However, the object of the exercise is clarity of presentation and the alternative - to use hatching at closer pitch - would take almost as long.

Representing materials in section

This was an almost universal practice when I was taught engineering drawing, more years ago than I care to remember. It is used today only in a very limited way (chiefly on assembly drawings) as material specifications are very tight now and should always be laid down in detail in a schedule. However, we do have to use 'old' drawings occasionally, and there are times (as we have just seen) where an indication is helpful. **Fig. 39** shows both the old and the current recommended conventions. Current practice is stated against each example first, current permitted and often-useful practice is shown in brackets (ferrous alloys) and the old or historical practice in

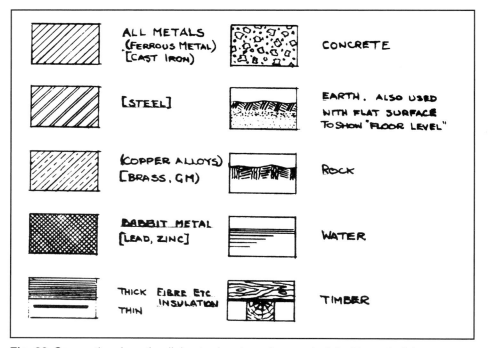

Fig. 39 *Conventional section lining to denote various materials. Those in ( ) are permitted, those in [ ] are not encouraged but may be found on old drawings.*

square brackets [cast iron]. So, plain hatching nowadays shows all metals. Perhaps 50 years ago this would have been used only for cast iron and the steels, with alternating plain and dotted lines for copper alloys. But my father would have used plain lines only for cast iron, double lines for steel and wrought iron, plain-and-dotted for brass and gunmetal and other combinations for bronze, zinc, copper and so on. On pictorial drawings the use of contrasting types of line can be useful, but they should be avoided on detail drawings unless they are essential. One small point: the convention for 'earth' is sometimes drawn with a straight horizontal line at the top on general arrangement drawings, to indicate floor level.

Section 4

Dimensioning

The dimensions are, of course, the essential feature of any drawing, whether it be a rough sketch or an elaborate detail drawing. This is the one region where it is *vital* that the proper conventions be observed. A faulty hidden detail line or an error in projection can usually be sorted out, given time. But a faulty dimension can be fatal. It is an unfortunate fact that it is just in this field of dimensioning that the amateur draughtsman tends to ignore the rules. It cannot be too strongly emphasised that these rules have been distilled from the experience of hundreds of thousands of workshops over the last 150 years or so of disastrous mistakes caused by poor dimensions. They have found out the hard way, and you will only run into trouble if you ignore them. After all, you do take a pride, quite justifiable, in both your workmanship and in your interpretation of the idea of being 'true to the prototype'. The drawing you make is *part* of the manufacturing process, and you ought to take as much

pride in getting it right as you do over your turning and fitting.

The following sections are illustrated with sketches. These are all very simple, and intended only to show the particular principle.

Scales

Before going into detail on dimensions themselves, perhaps a few words about the scale of the drawing will be helpful. This is nothing to do with the scale of the model you are building —that can be anything you please. (A very popular model railway scale is 0.138 inches to the foot, or 1/86.975.) The drawing itself, however, will be to one of a few standard ratios. Wherever possible parts should be drawn full size, as this eases visualisation of the object being made. However, if it is a very small part it is always prudent to enlarge it on the paper, again in one of the standard ratios, while if the object is too large to fit the available size of paper, then a standard reduced scale must be used. The standards are as follows.

Imperial Dimensions	Metric Dimensions
Full size	Full size
Enlarged drawings	
2/1	2/1
4/1	5/1
Reduced drawings	
Half size (1/2)	Half size (1/2)
Quarter size (1/4)	1/5
1/8	1/10
1/12	1/20

Structural drawings may be reduced even more than the above e.g. 1/96 or 1/100 if metric. On imperial drawings these ratios may be stated as 'x inches to the foot' and these are also used by ship modellers. But for workshop drawings such scales should be avoided, the scales being stated as shown in the table above (e.g. 1 inch to the foot as 1/12). In passing, it should be noted that there is no such thing as a one inch scale. One inch to the what? Foot, mile, rod, pole or perch? Avoid such statements; although they are in common usage, they can only cause confusion to someone used to thinking in, for example, metres.

Providing the scale of the drawing lines up with those given in the table you will be able to buy boxwood scales all marked out with feet and inches, or metres and millimetres, at the correct scale. Which you choose is up to you, but my own experience has taught me to use full size for choice if the sheet of paper is large enough (in which connection the standard sizes of paper are given at the end of the book).

General principles

Most of these are obvious, but still need stating, for many are often forgotten. The basic principle is that sufficient, but no more than sufficient, dimensions should be given to allow the part to be made.

(a) Each dimension should appear once only. An exception may be made where a long object has complex features at each end, when repetition may ease interpretation of other dimensions.

(b) Dimensions should be so arranged that it is unnecessary to arrive at one of them by addition or subtraction of others.

(c) On no account should any dimension be obtained by scaling the drawing. The reason for this is that the reproduction processes used cause a dimensional change in the paper. (The *exception* to this rule arises when a model is being designed from an undimensioned general arrangement drawing. However, when this is necessary it is only prudent to establish some *known* dimension and check that no serious error will result.)

(d) As far as possible each feature of the part should be dimensioned on a single view rather than on several. However, it is preferable to show a further view rather than to load a single one with too many dimensions. **Fig. 40 (a)** is preferred to **40 (b).**

(e) Functional dimensions i.e. those that affect the way in which the part works, should be clearly distinguished from the less important dimensions, as suggested in the sketch, **Fig.4l. (f)** It is preferable to use 'general notes' at the foot of the drawing rather than individual notes having identical meaning to each part. For example:

All fillets to be 5mm rad.

Drill sizes in mm., all other dimensions

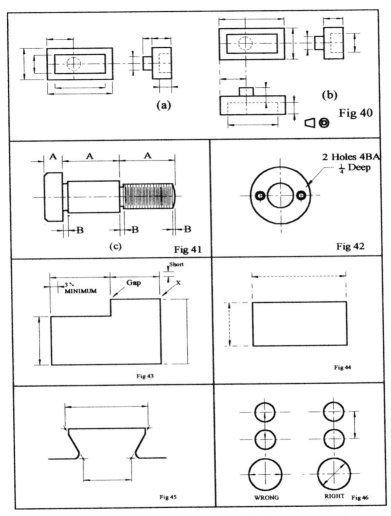

Fig. 40. *Examples of "preferred" (a) and "undesirable" (b) methods of dimensioning.* **Fig. 41** *"A" are "Functional"; "B" are "Non-functional" and "C" is an "Auxiliary"* .**Fig. 42** *Use of a note to provide dimensional information.* **Fig. 43** *. Extension and dimension lines in current "preferred" practice.* **Fig. 44.** *Dimension lines as found on older drawings – NOT good practice.* **Fig. 45** *Use of dots to emphasise point from which dimension is measured.* **Fig. 46** *Dimensions should never lie on centrelines.*

43

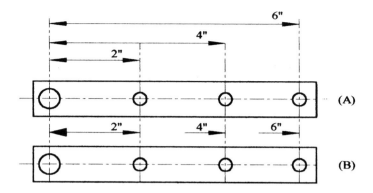

Fig. 46A. *Dimensioning from a common datum. "A" is preferred but "B" is permitted where space is limited. Note the "block" arrow at the datum in case "B".*

in inches.

Spotface all holes in castings.

Local notes should be set as near to the relevant point as possible. Long 'leaders' (see below) should be avoided (see **Fig. 42**).

Dimensions, extension lines and leaders

(Note Extension lines are often known as 'projection' lines.)

(a) Dimension and extension fines are shown in Fig. 43. Wherever possible, dimension lines
should lie outside the outline of the part.

(b) Extension lines are thin, and start just clear of the object lines. It is acceptable that there be a short dash at this end of the line, as at 'x'.

(c) Dimension lines should be thin, full lines, terminating in arrowheads not less than 3mm long. Note that on drawings made many years ago dimension lines were dotted - **Fig. 44**. This could lead to confusion with hidden detail and should not be used.

(d) Where an extension line refers to a point, there should be no gap, and it is acceptable that a small dot be set at the point of intersection for emphasis, **Fig. 45**.

(e) Centrelines should never be used as dimension lines. See **Fig. 46**.

(f) Dimension lines should never emerge as an extension of an outline but should be spaced away from it.

(g) Where several dimensions originate from a common reference plane, as in **Fig. 46A**, the dimensions should normally be as shown at (a). However, if space is short the method (b) may be used. Note the enlarged arrowhead at the reference plane, and that the dimensions are set close to the opposing arrowheads.

(h) Leaders are lines that indicate where notes or isolated dimensions are intended to apply. **Fig. 47** shows several examples. Leaders may terminate either with arrowheads or dots, arrows terminating ON

44

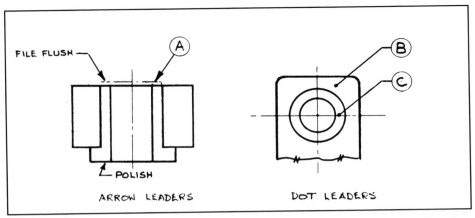

Fig. 47 *Leaders and notes. Arrows finish ON the surface and dots are used within the body of the part.*

a line, dots within the body of the object.

(i) While extension and dimensions may cross others, leaders should *never* cross leaders; the notes should be so positioned that this is not necessary.

Dimensions

(1) Units

(a)   If in feet and inches, *either* use 5ft 2in, or *5' 2"*; not a mixture such as 5ft 2". If feet are included, inch dimensions should be fractional; *5'- 7½*, not *5' 7.5"*. If decimal fractions of the inch size are necessary, then the whole dimension must be in inches — 67.42". *All* dimensions of 24 inches and below are stated solely in inches.

(b)   If all dimensions on the drawing are in inches, or all in millimetres, then the symbol " or mm may be omitted, but a note *must* be set on the drawing in a clear position stating the units used.

(c)   Metric dimensions should be millimetres. *Centimetres are forbidden.* For on-site drawings or drawings of structures, metres and decimals may be preferable e.g. 140.5, *not* 140m 500mm.

(2) Fractions

(a)   As has already been explained, fractions should have the bar horizontal, not sloping, $\frac{1}{2}$ not 1/2. An exception *may* be made when space is restricted, but this should be avoided wherever possible.

(b)   The practice of stating (e.g.) $\frac{57}{64}$ as $\frac{7}{8} + \frac{1}{64}$ is discouraged by BSI, but it does help those who are not using 'sixty-fourths' all day long. It should be used only for the larger fractions, however, and only for sixty-fourths.

(c)   It should be noted that a fractional dimension implies a 'rule' dimension unless it is qualified by a tolerance or limit. The words 'ream' and 'bore' applied to a fractionally dimensioned

45

hole do imply that it should be dead size — or as near as your worn reamer will allow. The note 'Std' (Standard) to a hole has the same implication, though the 'standard' will be that particular works' standard tolerance (tolerances are dealt with later).

(3) Decimal fractions

(a)   We have already noticed a few rules on **page 45.** You will recall that figures less than one should *always* be preceded by zero - 0.625. On dimensions especially the decimal

point should always be very bold and positive, and should be allotted a space as wide as the figure 6. The . is an unobtrusive little fellow and we must give it prominence.

(b)   Even though the drawing may be decimally dimensioned, it is still in order - and desirable - to give inch drill sizes in fractional form e.g. l/2" drill rather than 0.5" drill.

(c)   On the other hand, when using sheet or wire gauges, or letter and number drills, it is preferable to indicate the size in decimals (or mm on metric

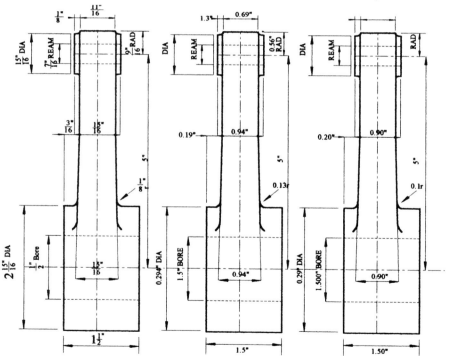

Fig. 47A *"Imperial" Dimensions (a) in fractions; (c) in decimals. The "Fractional Conversion" shown at (b) is NOT recommended - (a) or (c) is "preferred".*

drawings) as well. Thus: 16 swg (0.064").

(d) The implications of the 'significant figures' in a decimal dimension must always be kept in mind. It is *not* sufficient simply to translate the fraction into a decimal.

The dimension 5/8" is a rule dimension. Stated as 0.625" it immediately becomes a very close dimension indeed. The third significant figure implies that there *might* be a fourth, lying between 0.0005 below and 0.0004 above i.e. that it is between 0.6245 and 0.6254 rounded off to 0.625. If you start using 32s and 64s in decimals you can run into worse trouble - 7/64" is fair enough, but 0.109375" means that you must work to a millionth.

The RULE is that you should use no more significant figures than are absolutely necessary. Thus 5/8" might be 0.6" for a cored hole, 0.63" for a drilled one, and 0.625" only when reamed. Similar considerations apply to all decimal dimensions. The situation does not apply to a great degree in industry, as drawings are increasingly dimensioned in millimetres. For those who wish to, or who must, retain imperial dimensioning there are three alternatives. First, stick to fractions, applying tolerances as necessary. Second, convert to decimals but take *very great care* over significant figures. Or, third, abandon fractional equivalents altogether and change to true decimals of inches, just as we do in millimetres.

This last is the logical thing to do, but it is important to note that the whole design must be in decimals. Forget 3/8 - this now becomes 0.40 for a rule dimension and 0.400 for an exact one. (Decimal imperial rules are usually scaled in fiftieths or 0.02";

it is difficult to read one scaled in hundredths.) I have tried to illustrate this in **Fig. 47A**. At (a) is a lever dimensioned in fractions and (b) is the sort of result which appears all too often when a designer attempts to be 'with it' by using decimals. It is *quite* in order to quote '7/16 inch ream', as readers may not have truly decimal reamers. But simply to round off fractions to the nearest 0.01 inch results in very odd and sometimes difficult measurements. At (c) I have shown a similar lever as it might be designed in decimals from the start. You can see the difference immediately, although you may not agree with some of the degrees of accuracy implied by some of the significant figures which I have used (my sketch is intended only to show the general idea). My own practice is to use old-fashioned imperial fractions, sometimes with decimal tolerances, for most of my work, but to use purely metric design and dimensions where the class of work demands it. I deal with the conversion of imperial drawings in metric and vice versa on page 103.

In this connection, it is worth noting that there is absolutely *no* objection to quoting 'l/2-inch ream' on a metric drawing; this is just as reasonable as to quote '12mm drill' or even 'Drill No. 23' on an imperial drawing. It will be a long time before such crossover specifications disappear; not until all our reamers, mandrels, plug gauges and the like wear out.

(4) Angles

The significant figure rule can apply to angles also. Thus 25-l/2° would be a simple protractor measure. The same dimension, stated at 25° 30' implies accuracy to one minute and would need a vernier protractor. Finer than this would need very special

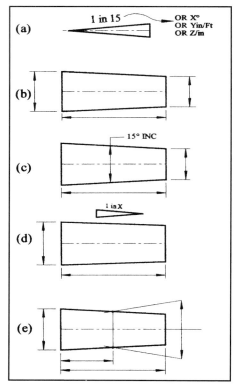

Fig. 48 *Methods of dimensioning tapers. The international symbol is shown at (a) - note that it has a centreline and that the taper is always stated on the diameter or the width.*

equipment indeed, but for the record, would be stated in degrees, minutes and seconds of arc, thus: 27° 35' 30". Angles less than one degree should always show the zero degrees, thus: 0° 25'.

(e) Tapers

The dimensioning of tapers can be tricky. There is no problem with the 'standards' - Morse, Jacobs, Brown & Sharpe etc - and

recognised abbreviations save space, No.3M, J6, or No.2 B &S.

Fig. 48 shows various methods of dimensioning other tapers. At (a) is the conventional symbol for a taper, and used in this way the taper quoted on it is always measured on the diameter or width of the object. The symbol may be used even when sufficient data is given by dimensions, simply to call attention to the fact that there is a taper. Note in examples (b), (c) and (d) there must be no more than *three* defining figures: two diameters and the length, or one diameter, the angle and the length. To give two diameters and the angle would require some mathematics by the machinist and is not approved.

The special case shown at (e) does appear to have four dimensions, but one

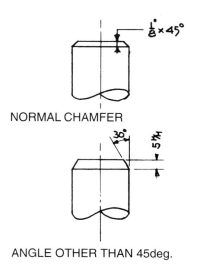

NORMAL CHAMFER

ANGLE OTHER THAN 45deg.

Fig. 49 *Chamfers. The angle must always be defined to a surface if other than 45deg.*

of these merely defines the position of one of the diameters. It is permissible to describe a taper 'to fit part xxx', but it must still be fully dimensioned; the 'to fit' is, in effect, an implied tolerance. Chamfers can be dimensioned simply by stating the width and the angle, noting that this angle must be defined to a surface as in **Fig. 49** it is other than 45°.

Setting out dimensions

There are a few basic and very important rules here, coupled with a vast range of good and bad practices. These

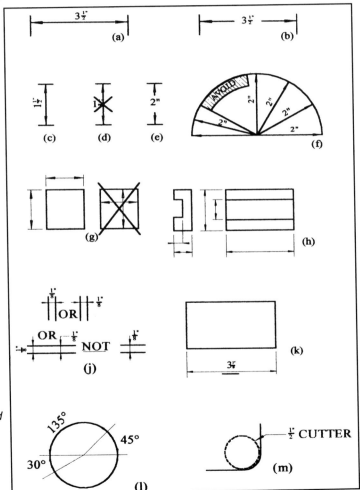

Fig. 50 *Setting out dimensions. The points are explained in the text, but note that method (e) is "permitted" only in exceptional circumstances.*

are inevitable, as each drawing is different, and what may be quite acceptable on one may make another almost unintelligible. First, the rules.

(1) Figures and letters should stand at *right-angles* to the dimension line, and slightly away from them, as at **Fig. 50 (a).** The earlier practice of setting the figure *within* the length of the line as at (b) is not recommended, but is acceptable when circumstances demand. Figures set on vertical or near vertical lines should be arranged to be read from the right-hand side of the drawing sheet, as at (c). Figures should NOT be set as shown at (d).

Contravention of this rule is one of the most common faults in amateur circles. It springs, I believe, from a reluctance to use stencils in the vertical plane or at an angle —another argument for using freehand figures. But it is quite WRONG. On the face of it, it doesn't matter, but if I were to write down all the examples of workshop mistakes which I know to have sprung from this practice it would take several pages.

Clearly there will be occasional exceptions. Where such are absolutely unavoidable then the figures should be *set* within the dimension line as at **Fig. 50e.** As seen in **Fig. 50f** there is an awkward area in which it is difficult to set dimensions, and this should be borne in mind when making the drawing.

(2) Wherever possible dimensions should be set *outside* the object lines, with the longest dimensions outside the shorter ones, as **Fig. 50g** and (**h**). Where a dimension can be applied to two views of the object it should be set between the views, as at (**h**). Note that the extension lines should spring from one view only.

(3) Where there is no room for the figures on the dimension line itself one of the arrangements of **Fig. 50j** should be used.

(4) If a feature on a drawing is not drawn to scale the dimension figures must be underlined, **Fig. 50k.** (This circumstance may arise when the design of a part undergoes a minor alteration.)

(5) Angles should be dimensioned with the figures disposed horizontally, as shown at **Fig.50l.** In the case of a large angle, however, the figures may be set along the arc if this adds clarity to the drawing.

(6) Circles must be dimensioned by giving the *diameter* but *arcs* by their *radius*. An exception may be made to this latter rule when the arc is to be formed by machining e.g. with a slot drill. In that case the practice shown in **Fig. 50m** may be followed.

(7) The rules for dimensioning keyways are shown on **Fig. 51.** These are, I think, clear enough, the obvious way. The dimensions on the drawing correspond to the measurement you would take with your rule or calipers - not a bad plan to follow in all dimensioning. (a) and (b) are for ordinary keys, the rest for the Woodruffe type.

(8) A very important rule. If any dimension must be altered once a print has been issued it must be crossed out, NOT erased, and the new figure set alongside. A reference letter should be set with the new figure and a note at the foot of the drawing should give the date of the alteration and its nature. Thus: (C) 21/11/02. 1/2 becomes 12mm; Ballrace changed to type FAG6001.

This rule need not, of course, be followed while you are actually making the drawing, but even if it is one which will be used only in your own workshop it is prudent to follow the rule once you have started using the drawing.

General dimensioning practice

Unless good practice is followed confusion can still result even if all the rules are strictly observed. To detail this in words would take many pages, so I have tried to distil the most obvious points into a few examples, see **Fig. 52**. At (**a**) is the correct way of dimensioning a cylinder; (**b**) and (**c**) are to be discouraged as a waste of space, extra work and the drawing is not very clear. Illustrated at (**d**) is the principle of setting

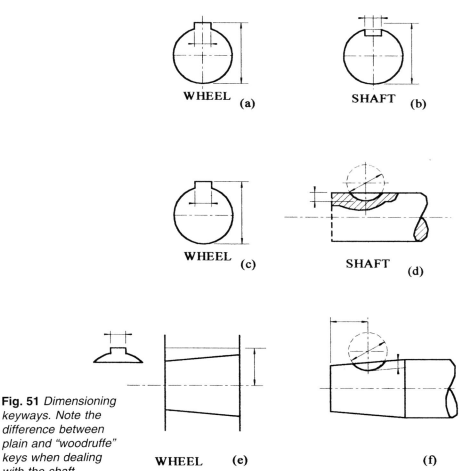

Fig. 51 *Dimensioning keyways. Note the difference between plain and "woodruffe" keys when dealing with the shaft.*

WHEEL (a)   SHAFT (b)

WHEEL (c)   SHAFT (d)

WHEEL (e)   (f)

out the dimensions clearly. It also illustrates the use of '∅' meaning diameter thereby saving space. Note that each dimension is set where it will be measured and that even though the two flats dictate the use of end elevation the diameters are still shown on the front view. At (e) is shown the use of a 'note' that gives all the necessary data about the holes without any dimensioning on the object itself. This is good practice for symmetrical pieces. but will not serve if the holes are not equally spaced or differ

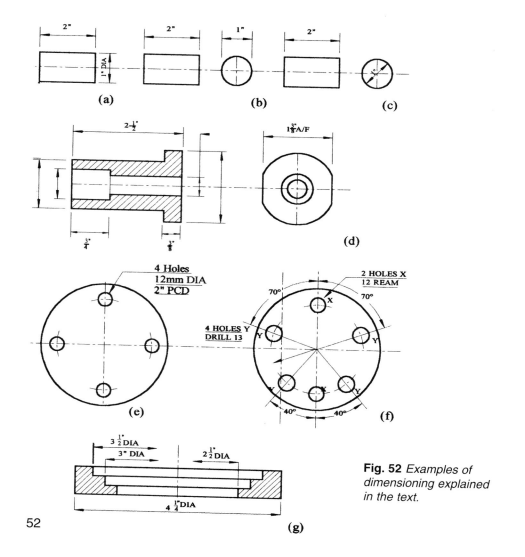

Fig. 52 *Examples of dimensioning explained in the text.*

in diameters, (**f**) shows the method for this case. Note that instead of having a large number of leaders from the note to each hole, the holes are identified by letter. Some draughtsmen set a cross within circles representing holes that need special treatment. A convenient method of dimensioning large diameters where space is limited is shown at (**g**).

The *positioning of holes* is covered in Fig. 53. The convention shown at (**a**) implies that the two holes are equidistant

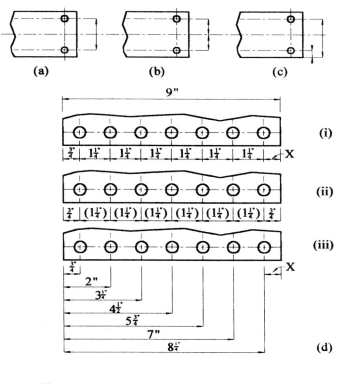

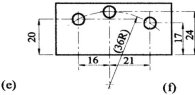

Fig. 53 *(a) to (d) positioning of holes. (e) and (f) use of auxiliary dimensions.*

53

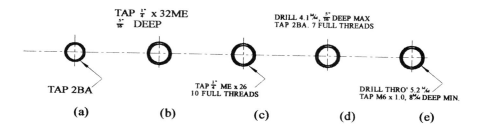

Fig. 54 *Methods of dimensioning tapped holes.*

from the centreline, and will (or should be) so interpreted by the driller whereas (**b**) is a more positive indication and the driller will take more care so should always be used in preference to (**a**) where space permits. At (**c**) the method of dimensioning indicates that the distance of the holes from the edge of the strip is more important than their spacing. Sketch (**d**) illustrates the common case of a row of holes. Method (i) is acceptable, but there is an implication that must not be forgotten. Unless set out with a jig borer the dimension 'x' may be up to 0.060 inch (or 1-1/2mm) oversize or undersize due to errors in marking out. This may not matter, but if the two end holes must line up with a set running at right angles, then the method shown at (ii) is preferred. Note that the spacing dimension is shown in brackets, as it is now a redundant dimension. Where the position of the holes is important throughout, then the co-ordinate method of (iii) should be used. If this is done the maximum error at 'x' will be very small.

Sketch (**e**) shows another application of a redundant dimension. It is a principle that where a series of dimensions is given

the sum should not be shown as a separate figure. The whole length of the part can be obtained by adding the 1 inch and the 4 inch. However, it is also a rule that the machinist should *not* have to add things up, and he needs to do so in this case to decide how much stock to saw off. So, the total length in this case is given in brackets. If this overall length was important, then one of the others would be set in brackets and the 5 inch defined. Another application of a redundant dimension is shown at (**f**). Here the holes are positively located by co-ordinates. But the fact that they also lie on the arc of a circle is shown in brackets.

Tapped holes must often be dimensioned on the face of the workpiece, and this must be done with some thought, see **Fig. 54**. Where the depth of neither the thread nor the tapping drill matters (**a**) is adequate. Further, the thread is fully described by the letters BA. The depth of thread is specified at (**b**), leaving the driller to determine how deep the drill must go - this depends on the type of tap used. *Note* that the type of thread is fully defined. Normally 1/4 x 40 can be taken to imply the M.E. thread form, but overseas

Fig. 55 *(a) and (b) Examples of unnecessary views and poor dimensioning practice. (c) A redundant view and duplicated dimension. Note also the impossible decimal dimensions on the hole centres.*

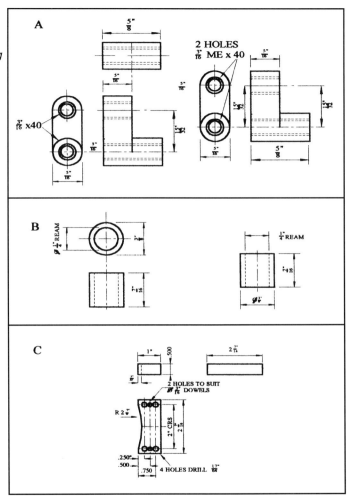

machinists may not realise this; so, the letters ME are included. Similarly at (**c**). In this case the depth is stated in terms of the number of fully formed threads required in the hole whereas (**d**) takes matters rather further. The designer requires a definite

depth of thread engagement and has stated the tapping drill size. (This is good practice anyway as the driller should not be expected to look up his tables every time.) the maximum depth of drill is defined - for example to prevent fouling another hole -

55

and the depth is given again in terms of the number of full threads (which will be less than the number of turns on the tap-wrench if the tap is not a bottoming type). Finally, at (**e**) we have a through hole, and the depth of tapping is given as a minimum required to ensure adequate design strength.

Of these methods, (**a**) is very common, but (**b**) or (**c**) are to be preferred. On drawings made for my own use I always show the tapping drill, to save time in the shop, and generally state depth in terms of number of threads. This saves walking across the shop to look at the chart and it is easier to count turns than to lay a rule on the tap.

Finally, **Fig. 55** shows three examples taken from published drawings that will bear examination. On the left of (**a**) is the drawing as supplied, though I have added a line that was missing. There is little to fault on the dimensioning - as I have redrawn it the rules are followed. However, I show on the right the preferred method; this saves a view, the centre distance that relates to two views lies between them and it has taken the draughtsman less time to make. I would accept a criticism of my alternative, in that the note to the two tapped holes could be better placed - as it was on the original, in fact. My fault - that is the proper place, but I did not leave enough room on the paper.

Example (**b**) is the classic case of the redundant view. The inverted plan tells us nothing except that the object is round and this is clear from the use of the symbol for diameter. The sketch on the right shows the proper way. Note that there is no $\emptyset$ on the 1/4 inch ream dimension; unnecessary as you cannot ream anything but a diameter.

At (**c**) we have not only a redundant view, but also a duplicated dimension. The top right - hand view gives us no information which is not provided by the other views. You may notice some other slips, but I leave you to find them for yourself. (Holes B are drilled.)

Section 5

Conventional Representation

To draw every part of a workpiece in full detail would be very time-consuming and would also be likely to make the drawing less readable. This particularly applies to parts that are often repeated, such as screw threads. Over the years, therefore, draughtsmen have developed many conventions or symbols to replace the detail representation of the feature these have gradually been standardised on a more or less international basis. I have already dealt with those referring to the sectioning of different materials on page 40. **Figs 56** and **57** illustrate those referring to machine parts. In almost every case the convention is a stylised version of the appearance of the finished part.

In **Fig. 56** are those for screw threads: (**a**), (**b**) and (**c**) show a semi-pictorial type for external, internal in section, and thread in hidden detail. Neither the pitch nor the core diameter are strictly to scale but should be in good proportion. Note that the extra penetration of the tapping drill is shown. This is a simple method, very clear even to a layman, and about the only way in which a male thread may be sectioned to show internal detail as at (**d**). It is very easy to

draw, though can be ragged if hurried.

The type shown at (**a**), (**f**) and (**g**) was the British Standard preferred for many years. The thin lines represent the tops of the threads and the thick ones the root. Again, neither pitch nor core diameter need be accurately to scale. Draughtsmen would reverse their tee-squares on the board and use the tapered backs to get the slight angle to the lines. Note that (**a**) shows a right-hand thread and so does (**b**), although it appears to be reversed; this is because you are seeing the *back* of the thread in section. In more recent years the lines were drawn without slope, as at (**h**). There is no disadvantage, as the type of thread must be specified anyway.

The current British Standard convention is shown in (**j**), (**k**) and (**l**). Note the line showing the depth of full thread, and the slight taper beyond it to indicate the imperfect threads at the ends. It is clearly much quicker to draw than either of the other conventions.

All three methods are acceptable, and you can choose that which suits you best. However, for amateur use I would avoid the third type (**j**) to (**l**). It does not *look* like a

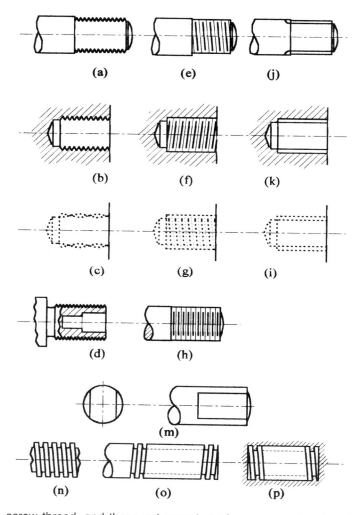

Fig.56 *Conventional representation of screw threads.*

(a) (e) (j)

(b) (f) (k)

(c) (g) (i)

(d) (h)

(m)

(n) (o) (p)

screw thread, and those not accustomed to it may be confused especially when shown in hidden detail. I have the further objection to it that to the amateur drawer-reader it can be confused with a shaft bearing two flats — see sketch (**m**). For all my own drawings I use the first method, (**a, b, c**). It is very clear, particularly in hidden detail, and I don't find it difficult to make a presentable job of the outline. I do use method (**h**) occasionally, but never in hidden detail, as the drawing becomes a mass of dotted lines. A male thread in section is impossible with any method other than (**d**). Square and Acme threads cannot be shown by similar conventions. **Fig. 56** (**n**) is the pictorial convention - it is not a true projection, as the lines are all straight instead of being curves. This is used on presentation drawings i.e. those where an impression must be created. But on working drawings these threads are shown as at (**o**) and (**p**) for male and sectioned female threads respectively. (Hidden detail would be shown as at (**o**) but dotted lines.) The same convention is used for Acme threads unless they are large enough to draw the proper Acme profile, which is seldom. Both square and Acme threads must be defined by notes anyway, so there is no need to distinguish the conventions.

Springs are indicated in a number of ways, but those shown in **Fig. 57** (**a**) and (**b**) are preferred: (**a**) is a compression spring, and you will see that the semi-pictorial representation enables the type of end to be indicated clearly although it should also be defined in a note.

Similarly, with the tension spring (**b**) the type of end can be indicated. It is good practice for these ends to be detailed in a scrap view alongside the spring so that they

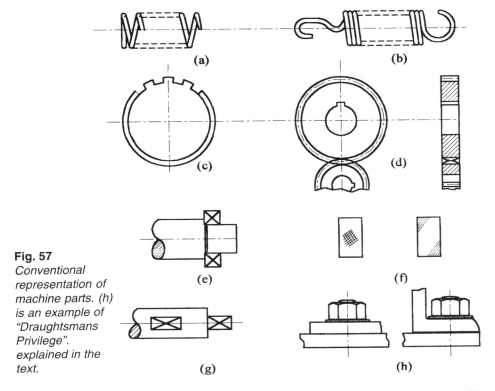

Fig. 57
Conventional representation of machine parts. (h) is an example of "Draughtsmans Privilege". explained in the text.

can be properly dimensioned. Splines and gears carry teeth, the drawing of which could be a labour and an unnecessary labour at that. The convention is that one or two teeth only are drawn and then indicated as in **Fig. 57** (**c**) and (**d**). The spline and tooth form are, of course, defined in a note. In the case of gears the pitch circle should be drawn. In the sectional view on the right you can see two methods of indicating the teeth. At the top a chain-dotted line is drawn on the pitch circle; where the two wheels meet I have shown a couple of diagonal lines, either can be used. There is no need to detail ball or roller bearings, the convention at (**e**) will suffice. The same symbol is used for both, the type being defined in a note. Alongside at (**f**), are the symbols for knurling Some draughtsmen like to hatch the complete area but this is unnecessary for a workshop drawing although desirable on assembly and general arrangements. Flats and squares are usually shown on end views or sections, but can be indicated on elevations as at (**g**). To end this section, a case of draughtsman's privilege. In any NVQ examination the projection of a hexagon nut in the way seen at (**h**) would lose marks, but it is common in commercial drawings - I always draw them this way on design drawings. The reason is that we see the nut taking up the maximum amount of room in both views, and so can check that the nut can, in fact, be turned. The one situation where we do show two flats of the hexagon would be where we wish to have one flat of the bolt-head hard up against a web so that it is prevented from turning when fitting the nut.

There are a number of other conventions, of course, but they are of less interest to the amateur. Full details can be obtained by reference to British Standard No. 308 (at your local public library).

Section 6

Tolerances

There is some confusion over both the nature and purpose of tolerances on dimensions. In particular, many people speak of a tolerance when they mean an allowance. An allowance is the difference between the dimensions of two mating parts necessary to allow them to work. Thus a shaft may be 0.03mm or 0.001" less in diameter than a bush, to provide a sliding fit, or the same amount larger than the hole to result in a drive fit. This allowance emerges automatically when the part is dimensioned, and normally is provided on the shaft; the hole is best machined to the standard dimension.

A tolerance is quite different. It is the difference between the largest and smallest size that will permit the part to serve its function. In the case of the allowance just mentioned, if the hole were 1.000 inch diameter, then the 'perfect' shaft would be 0.999 inch diameter. It would still slide if it were 0.9995, but might be too sloppy if it were 0.998 inch diameter. That being so, the tolerance would be 0.9995 - 0.998 = 0.0015 inches. This is the greatest difference that can be 'tolerated' by the designer of the machine, hence the name.

It is to be noted, especially by the amateur, that the application of a tolerance does not result in greater accuracy. It is just the opposite - a range of 'acceptability of error'.

Model engineers may well ask "Why have an error at all?" They pride themselves on working on the drawing. In fact, when making one-offs as we do, with one part made to fit another, there is no need for any tolerance although allowances are needed. If a normally 2 inch cylinder comes out at 1.998 inch diameter it doesn't really matter (except to our pride) and the piston, properly fitted, will serve its office. On a coarser dimension, it doesn't matter at all that a buffer beam be even 1mm too long, does it? The trouble arises when we stop making things one at a time, and have an output in the hundreds or thousands. Even more so, as the shaft, say, is made in one part of the works and the bush in another - or even in another country. In such circumstances the parts will be made on automatic or semiautomatic machines, N.C. lathes or capstans. If the tooling is set at 8 o'clock to give dead size, by dinner-time the workpieces will be coming out oversize due to tool wear (or grinding wheel wear for that matter). It is possible to make all parts dead to size, but very expensive indeed and desperately slow. So, in production work a tolerance is essential. The designer of the machine must lay down the limits of size which experience or experiment has shown will be acceptable. He will then have a battle royal with the production manager who wants tolerances as wide as possible for economic reasons and they will finally agree on a compromise acceptable both to the function of the machine and its cost. The tooling will be set up in the first instance to make the spindle (say) slightly undersize (the 'minimum metal' condition) and as the cutter wears the parts will gradually increase in size until they reach the largest acceptable diameter - the 'maximum metal' condition. The tooling must then be taken out and replaced or re-sharpened.

Now, circumstances can arise where a tolerance is needed even on a one-off. The classic case is the ball or roller bearing. The bore and the O.D. of the bearings will be made to a tolerance - they are making them by the thousand each week. Typical figures might be the bore 0.003mm large to 0.010 small - + 0.0001" to -0.0004". You need a tolerance on both your shaft and your housing, so that the desired fit on each can be achieved. Looking up in the catalogue you might find that the shaft should be machined to +0.003mm/+0.016mm and the housing to -0.003mml/-0.015mm. Any diameter between these ranges will give you the recommended light drive fit on the inner race and the push fit on the outer. You could, of course, take immense care to get the shaft exactly 0.01mm up and the bore 0.01mm down in size, but the advantage of the tolerance

system is that you have a reasonable margin within which to work.

It will be seen from this discussion that there should be little need for the model engineer to specify tolerances on his drawings. It may be necessary to define *allowances* e.g. the clearance between shaft and axlebox or pump ram and the bore - but this can easily be done by setting a note on the part (see **Fig. 58**). This is preferable to giving the dimension as 11.95mm, and this implies an unnecessary tolerance. The basic or nominal diameter is 12mm, and by defining this and the allowance the machinist can adjust the 'basic' to suit the possible error which may be present in the hole diameter. In this connection it is, perhaps, worth mentioning that wherever possible allowances should be made on the male component, with holes (if as usual, of reamed finish) being taken as at the standard basic dimension.

Defining tolerances

The preferred method of including a tolerance on a dimension is shown in **Fig. 59 (a)**. The upper and lower limits are shown with the maximum metal size first, and as complete dimensions. At (**b**) is an alternative for a hole that differs solely in the way in which the figures are disposed. The maximum metal size is shown first. The method shown at (**c**) defines the basic dimension and then shows the tolerance as a separate number - this is very common on older drawings. It suffers from the fact that the machinist has to do a little calculation to establish the sizes between which he must work.

An important rule. Toleranced dimensions must always be in decimals. For example, to write 1-1/2" ±0.002" is a contradiction,

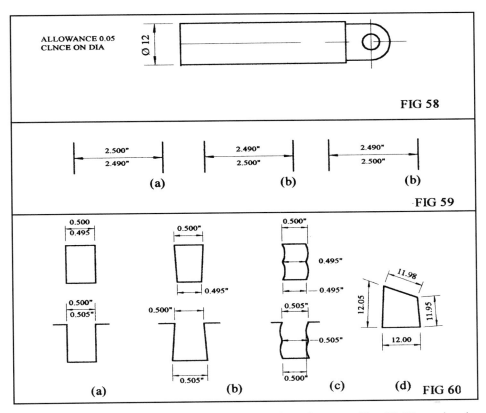

Fig. 58 *An "allowance".* **Fig. 59** *Methods if indicating tolerances.* **Fig. 60** *Dimensional tolerances do not necessarily ensure geometric accuracy.*

as the use of a fraction implies the general drawing tolerance. You will always find this on production engineering drawings in the title box in terms such as:

Tolerance ±0.02in. except where stated *or* Tolerance on all fractional dimensions ± 1/64" *or* Tolerance ±0.05mm except where stated.

To sum up this section, it is important to realize that setting tolerances on a dimension does not make the workpiece more accurate; the tolerance simply expresses the limits of error which will be acceptable in service. The application of an allowance, however, does ensure that the desired fit will, within the limits of error, be achieved. For one-off workpieces or even for multiple workpieces made by one-off methods, it is best to make the drawing to show the basic dimensions, and to leave

63

the tolerancing to the machinist who is actually making the piece. I have one lathe on which I can work to 0.0002 inch, but at least one Duke of Edinburgh Trophy-winning model was made on an old flatbed Drummond which would have had problems at ten times that limit. More depends on the turner than on the machine, the drawing, or the tolerances.

Interpreting tolerances

At first sight the effect of the tolerances shown in **Fig. 59** are evident; the dimension will lie between the limits shown, but there is more to it than that. Look at **Fig. 60**, where I show the effects of the same tolerance on various shapes; you will see at (**b**) and (**c**) that although within the limits and although the inspector's plug and gap gauges would show that all was well, the parts just 'fit where they touch'. At (**d**) is just one possible shape of a square which has been toleranced to 12 ±0.05mm (about 0.002"). (The distortion is, of course, exaggerated.)

Tolerances and manufacturing methods

You will recall the problem set up by possible errors in the pitch of a row of holes in **Fig. 53** (**d**). One solution to the difficulty outlined at (**i**) in that sketch would appear to be to tighten the tolerance - give the pitch as (say) 1.251/1.249". Then, if the errors were randomly distributed up and down, the dimension 'x' has a chance of lying between tolerances of the same order. But, and it is a big but, how are the holes to be machined? At that level of tolerance you have assumed that they will be bored on a jig-borer or on a first-class toolroom milling machine. So, this leads to the final point in interpreting tolerances. Where these define position rather than simply lengths or diameters you will have to think very carefully indeed about how you are to cope with them. With care (and, perhaps, with some resort to abrasive polishing.) you can work to 0.0001 inch on a centre-lathe, but locating a hole is quite another matter. Now look at **Fig.55** (**c**) again. This very brief discussion of tolerancing should not give the impression that the matter is unimportant. In all production shops it is of the greatest concern; selecting tolerances can make all the difference between a healthy profit and bankruptcy. B.S.308 has a complete volume on the subject and my copy of *Machinery Handbook* takes up several dozen pages of small print - as well as many tables giving the standard tolerances for everything from sheet metal to ball-bearings.

The model engineer, however, and the amateur machinist generally, will only be affected when the fit of a bought-in piece is involved. Use your judgement while doing the machining rather than putting tolerances on the drawing; no tolerance at all is *far* safer than one that is inappropriate.

Section 7

Machining Marks

There is absolutely no necessity for setting machining marks on parts made from rolled, drawn or extruded sections such as barstock etc. Such marks are, however, needed on castings and forgings. They are of prime importance to the patternmaker or forgemaster, so that additional metal can be left on to allow for machining. The machine-shop finds the indications useful in drawing attention to the parts of a casting which will need machining. It is easy enough on our small drawings, but when you come to an engine casting which may weigh 20 tons, the drawing of which carries several hundred dimensions, every little helps.

The original symbol was the letter 'f' set across or on the surface to be machined; **Fig. 61 (a)**. This originally meant 'finish' and 150 years ago implied the use of a file more often than a machine. Later, as finer finishes were required we find drawings carrying f, ff, and fff, each indicating a finer degree of finish. However, this could cause confusion, and in my days in the drawing office we used 'f' alone except where the surface was to be ground, when we wrote in 'g'; the surface finish needed, if special, was given in a note on the drawing. Where all parts were to be machined all over the 'f' was left off the individual parts and a note 'machine all over' set in the title block to the drawing.

Later, the triangle symbol shown in **Fig. 61(b)** was used instead of the letter - it took up less room and was more striking. Again, this could be repeated as in the case of the 'f' to indicate the more refined finishes.

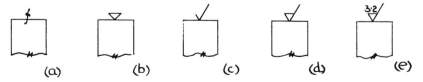

Fig. 61 *Machining marks (a) on older drawings (b) immediate post-WWII standard. (c) 1953 standard, not recommended. (d) Current "preferred" symbol. (e) Machining mark with surface roughness number stated in Microns or micro-inches.*

Then, following US practice, the tick shown in **Fig. 61(c)** became the standard. It did not last long, as it was not conspicuous enough. The current symbol is that shown in **Fig. 61(d)** - a triangle with a tail. For what it is worth, BS 308 specifies that the triangle be equilateral, and the tail at 60°. If an indication of the fineness of the finish is deemed to be necessary this is to be stated by including the roughness figure, in either micro-inches on imperial drawings or microns on metric ones, as shown at **Fig. 61(e)** (that shown is in microns, about 125 micro-inches).

As in the case of tolerances, to specify surface finish requires considerable experience. Further, it cannot be checked without a very specialised piece of equipment. It is best to avoid any such indications on drawings for model engineers or amateur machinists. Quite apart from anything else, precision of dimension does not always walk hand-in-hand with an apparently high surface finish. A turned finish, for example, ranges from 250 m-in, when roughing to 16 when finishing and even 4 m-in. under really good conditions. Grinding can range from 64 to 4 m-in. reaching down to 1 m-in, with special care. The best advice I can give to the model engineer is simply to indicate which surfaces on a casting or forging need a machined surface, and leave it to the machinist to use his or her judgement. It is, however, often prudent to indicate to the patternmaker the amount of machining allowance required. The cylinder head castings for one of our engines needed no more than 0.015 inch, the castings being so accurate that they were simply machined on a surface grinder. Amateur foundrymen may need a rather larger allowance.

Section 8

Making Drawings and Sketches

Types of drawing

You can, of course, make a perfectly usable drawing with a felt pen or a piece of chalk. At the other extreme you may have seen drawings being produced on most elaborate draughting machines coupled to electronic display units. So, a few words on the types of drawing before dealing with how to make them.

I will start with the sketch. This is used for three main purposes.

(1)   To record an idea so that it is not forgotten later.

(2)   To record the measurements or shape of an existing piece of machinery.

(3)   To transfer information from (e.g.) a large drawing to the workplace - lathe or bench - where use of the drawing would be inconvenient.

Most readers will have had the experience of forgetting A sketch need only be very simple, just the bare bones, and needs no elaborate equipment. The back of an envelope is, however, unwise, as if it drops wrong way up it may get thrown away. Professional engineers keep an ideas book for them, much wiser, and I show in **Fig. 62** one taken from "The Life of Nasmyth" by Smiles showing the first sketch of his steam hammer. There is some suspicion that the 'almost to scale' drawing of the complete hammer, bottom left, was done later, but you will see that he has not only sketched the arrangement on the other view, but also worked out the essentials in figures, too. Incidentally, Nasmyth used both pen and pencil for these sketches, and you can see that he was a good draughtsman.

To illustrate the second type I show **Fig. 63** taken from one of my own books. This is what I call a hand sketch. No instruments are used, but as I use sectional books - ones which have the pages of squared paper - it is possible to show the component in its proper proportions, though not, of course, exactly to scale. A sketch of this type is usually done at leisure and with care, as a missed dimension could be serious. The paper is of very good quality to withstand erasure, and I use a sharp H grade pencil, sometimes lining in later. (This sketch was made over 40 years ago, and has worn well).

The third type of sketch is the most common, especially among jobbing

67

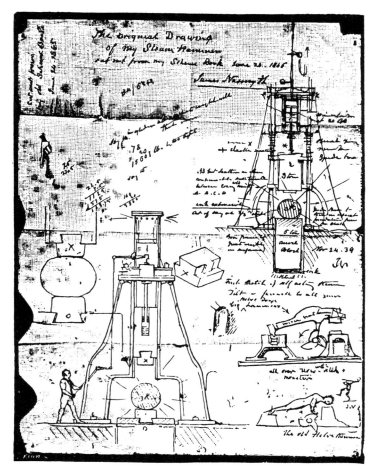

Fig. 62 *James Nasmyth's initial sketch of his steam hammer. (Smiles' "Life of Nasmyth" - 1895)*

workers and model engineers. In a confined workshop it is often difficult to find space for a large drawing (but, as we shall see later, most firms have now abandoned their use anyway) and if you are working from a book or a magazine it is unwise to have it within range of a suds pump. So, we make a sketch of the part and take this to the workplace. The procedure also enables us to incorporate alterations if we want to. See **Fig. 64**, which is my usual practice for small parts to be turned, the little blackboard being above the lathe. **Fig. 65** is a sketch on scrap paper of part of the Davey motor. You will see that it is both numbered and dated, as it is, in fact, the *only* detail drawing of this part, taken off from my general arrangement. You will also see that I had

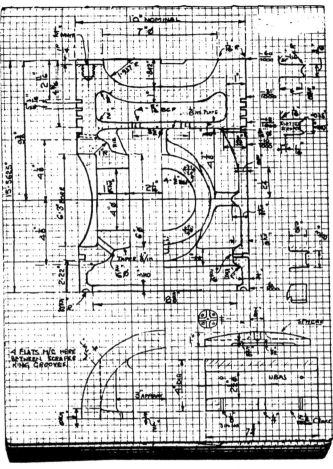

Fig. 63 *A "Hand Sketch" made by the author circa 1950 using pencil in a "Sectional Book" of squared paper. Note the use of a compound sectional view. (The decimal rendering of 9/16in was due to lack of space.*

second thoughts part way through and altered the design, but that is another matter. Such a sketch need not be to scale, can be quite rough, but it must be complete in its dimensions. I use any paper to hand - friends in offices save me paper due for shredding and I have also had stuff from the local stationery wholesaler 'damaged in transit' - very useful I use grade B pencils, ballpoint and even felt-tip pens.

The sum up the differences, the 'idea' sketch will be the bare bones on which you will fit the detail later. It should be reasonably permanent and preferably in a book. The second type should be carefully done, as accurate as freehand work will allow, and again permanent. The third is an ephemeral affair if it is a copy of another

69

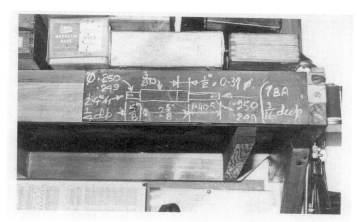

Fig. 64 *A "Workshop Sketch" in chalk on the author's blackboard above the lathe.*

drawing; this depends on what you are doing. It should be clear, the dimensions checked carefully, but the linework need not be as good as on the other types of sketch. Let us now look at the engineering drawing proper.

THE WORKSHOP DRAWING is the most familiar one, as it used to make the machine parts. It is drawn to scale, but the thickness of the lines and the subsequent reproduction processes (there may be several stages) means that it is unsafe to scale from the print itself. The prime requirement is boldness and absolute clarity, both in the way it is laid out and in the quality of the lettering and figures. **It is vital that all the rules be followed,** otherwise there is grave risk of misunderstanding by the machinist. This applies even if you are making the drawing solely for your own use - if, for no other reason, that you may come back to it in the future and may forget that you have taken liberties with the 'grammar'. The drawing is usually made on plain paper and then traced, but in many cases it is convenient to use semi-transparent paper from which a reasonable print can be taken even from pencil work. A medium hard pencil is used - I use 3H for centre and other thin lines and 2H for outlines, but I shall be coming to pencils shortly. In former times it was customary for *all* the detail parts for each component to appear on a single drawing making it rather large. Nowadays the more usual practice is to use a separate small sheet for *each* of the component parts - handier in the workshop and less expensive when the shop print has to be replaced. But the actual *size* of the drawing sheet must be sufficient to permit the various views to be laid out without crowding and to leave room for the notes which may be necessary. The drawing should contain *all* the information necessary for a competent machinist to make the part. In model engineering especially, there is a nasty habit of inserting a note saying 'refer to text' when a constructional article is involved. This is fair enough if the reference deals, say, with a hint on how to carry out the work; the article may be read by many who are

Fig. 65 *A "Workshop Sketch" made on scrap paper. Note the "floor to floor" machining times.*

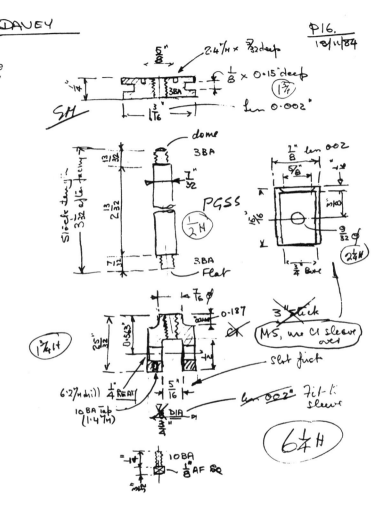

beginners in the 'art and mystery of turning' for example. But it is quite wrong to leave anything off the drawing, even if it means setting a fairly comprehensive note in the title box at the bottom. If the workshop drawing includes a number of parts, then reference numbers and a list in the title box should show the name of each, either immediately underneath it or. It should not really be necessary to say so but it *is* important to state the material of which each part is to be made, *and* the number

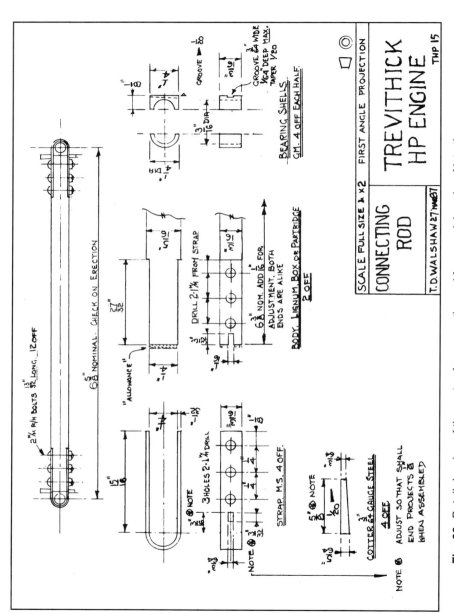

Fig. 66 *Detail drawing of the parts of a connecting rod for a model engine. Note the use of a title block. The sheet is A4 size, 210 x 297mm.*

required. It takes but seconds to write 'MS. Three off, but it is a nuisance having to look up a back number of a magazine to find out this information. **Fig. 66** is an example of a small drawing of this type, which includes all the parts (except some standard bolts) needed to make a rather unusual pair of connecting rods. It can be criticised in that the 'note' referring to the dimension of the slot in the strap is remote from the dimension - it would have been better to interchange of position of the note

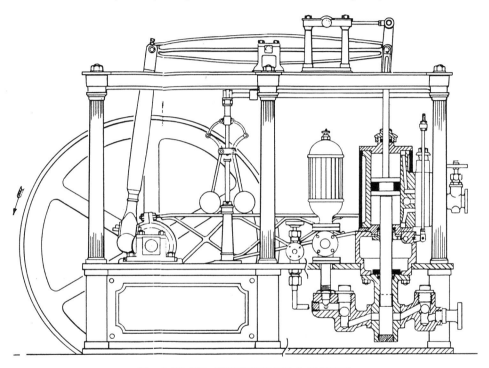

LADY STEPHANIE

A PUMPING ENGINE OF 3/4 HORSEPOWER FOR ESTATE USE

DESIGNED AND CONSTRUCTED

BY

MR TUBAL CAIN C.E.

Fig. 67 *A typical "assembly" drawing, part in section to show detail.*

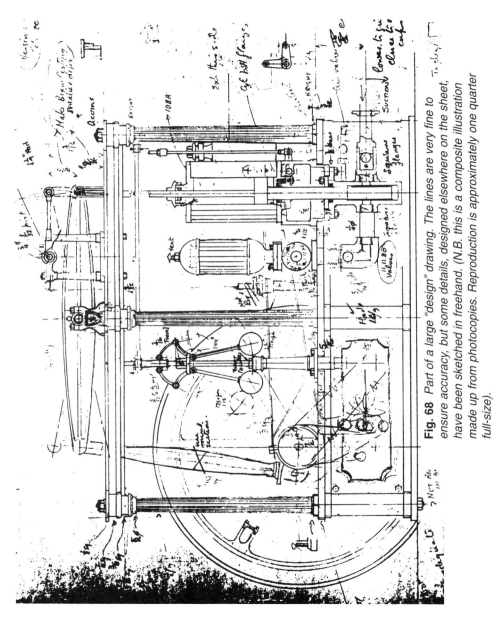

Fig. 68 Part of a large "design" drawing. The lines are very fine to ensure accuracy, but some details, designed elsewhere on the sheet, have been sketched in freehand. (N.B. this is a composite illustration made up from photocopies. Reproduction is approximately one quarter full-size).

74

and the drawing the cotter. The sheet was A4 size.

Almost as important is the ASSEMBLY DRAWING, as this is needed with few exceptions to guide the erector. This also is drawn to scale with some precision, and usually carries no dimensions other than those necessary either to give the eventual customer some idea of the size, or to indicate the normal length of some adjustable part. Considerable use will be made of sectional views, but it is not considered necessary to give sections of standard parts - valves, bearings, etc. - unless there is something special about them. Nor are sections necessary when a sub-assembly drawing carries both detail and arrangement views.

Accuracy and clarity are again essential, and some care is often needed in the choice of scale of the drawing, even on a large engine there may be some very small details. **Fig. 67** is an example that has served both as an assembly and as a display drawing. In this case detail assemblies took care of matters like the governor drive and the arrangement of the parallel motion linkwork. This drawing was on A3 size.

DESIGN DRAWINGS are seldom, if ever, seen outside the drawing office. These are the medium through which the designer converts his ideas into reality. They are, in part, ephemeral, as the india-rubber is as much an essential tool as the pencil. On the other hand, they are usually 'on the board' for far longer than any other type of drawing. This fact, and the need for *meticulous* accuracy demand special paper and also very hard, and hard pencils.

Unfortunately this makes it very difficult to reproduce them, **Fig. 68** shows the original design drawing for the engine shown in **Fig. 67**. You will see that the lines were (in the original drawing) very thin. Also, that some parts, designed separately, are merely sketched in freehand. There are notes, mere scribbles, all over the place. On the other hand, a singular paucity of dimensions; this is the exception to the rule, as the drawing *must* be sufficiently accurate to scale from if need be. (In practice, of course, there is an intermediate state between the design and the workshop drawing - that of detailing, which is a further design process in which individual parts are refined in design.) You will appreciate that **Fig. 68** shows only part of the drawing - the original was nearly 4ft long. I should add, too, that though **Figs 67** and **68** look very much alike, the former was *not* made from the latter. Assembly drawings must *always be* made using the details from the workshop drawings.

The tools for the job

We had better start with *pencils*. If all you need is something to make rough sketches then the ordinary HB pencil (perhaps with a rubber at the end) will serve, but for anything more than this you should obtain some of proper draughtsman 's quality. These are made by Royal Sovereign, Venus, Faber-Castell, Staedtler and others. The 'lead' (really graphite) is compounded to give a very uniform and black line. They are available in grades from about 6B to 9H. Tastes differ, but for what it is worth I use grade B for sketching, H for hand sketches, 2H and 3H for detail drawings, and 4H and 6H for design work - the harder grade for such things as centrelines and the softer for outlines. For dimensions and lettering H or 2H are used.

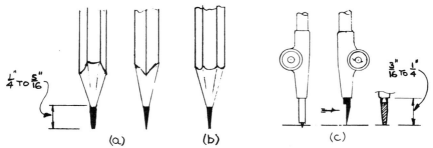

Fig. 69 *Pencil points. (a) for linework (b) for figures and letters (c) for compasses.*

You can obtain these in the classic wooden form, or as refillable holders. Again tastes differ - I find the collet-type holders a bit of a nuisance as if you have several grades it is difficult to tell which is which, whereas the wooden ones are clearly marked at the end. Make your choice

The critical matter is the sharpening. For all linework the 'point' should *not* be pointed, but more a chisel shape, **Fig. 69(a)**. This enables thin lines to be drawn with ease; in my younger days I could draw about 100 lines to the inch with a 6H pencil. The difference between thin and thick lines is obtained by changing the *grade* of the lead, not by using a blunter point. In passing, some drawing pencils are offered with flat leads, presumably to ease the making of the point. I have never found these to be any advantage. Best sharpening results can be obtained from a worn flat file, about 4 to 6 inch fine cut. The leads for compasses are sharpened in the same way, as shown in **Fig. 69** at (**c**). Pencils for lettering are, of course, filed to a conical point, **Fig, 69(b)**. (The wooden part is, of course, cut with a sharp penknife.)

Paper can be a problem if you don't do much drawing. Almost any sort will do for sketching. If you are not going to need prints

(copies can be made from pencil on a photocopier) then good quality typing paper - around 100 gm/sq.metre (gsm) - will serve quite well and this can be bought up to A3 size in most shops. Artists' supply shops can offer even larger sizes, but you should tell them what you want it for. A surface good for taking charcoal or watercolour, or even airbrush, is not suitable for hard pencil work. If you expect to do a lot of drawing, then a roll of detail paper or detail tracing paper is worthwhile - you can get prints made from the latter. It comes in 25 metre rolls, widths from 30 inches to 48 inches. I use this tracing paper, 90gsm in weight, natural tint and smooth finish, for most of my work. For serious design work, though, you need something more robust, and the hard, draughtsman's hot pressed cartridge-type paper is the ideal. It is by no means cheap, but the drawing will last for 100 years or more.

I have not referred to drawing in ink, or tracing on linen or film, and don't intend to. This is a job for the specialist - it takes longer to make a good tracer than it does to make a good draughtsman, I think. By all means try if you wish, but as you can get perfectly reasonable prints from pencil on tracing paper the only real need for inkwork is on tracings used either in large engineering works or for reproduction in a magazine. If you do need a tracing there are jobbing tracers to be found in the *Yellow Pages* who will do the work for you. Incidentally, the tracing paper I have mentioned above will serve for inkwork, but is less permanent than tracing cloth or film. (Note that it is *not* the flimsy stuff used by dressmakers and children for tracing patterns) You will need a drawing-board, and you can pay anything from a 'fiver' to well over £1000. Although I do have a simple draughting machine I also use a small plain drawing-board and tee-square for a great deal of work. This is 16 x 23 inches, half imperial or A2 in metric measure, and quite large enough for all but major design work. The next size down, A3 or 12 x 16 inches, is rather too small. The paper size is fair enough, but there is not enough elbow room on the board. Plain drawing-boards are either clamped or battened, **Fig. 70**. The former are quite

adequate for casual work, but it is worth getting one with a hard insert at the end. (You can, of course, make one for yourself with little trouble. They are made of yellow pine, which is very stable and will not warp.) With the board you will need a tee-square, also shown in **Fig. 70**. There is no need for the tapered type on such a small board, but again it is worth having a hard edge. Modern ones usually have a transparent plastic edge and this is an advantage; you can see what you have done just below the edge.

There are, of course, miniature drawing centres available, with parallel motion linkwork controlling the draughting head carrying straight-edges in place of a tee-square. However in the small sizes they are not quite as convenient on the kitchen table as they look It is not a bad rule to start with the simplest equipment and work up.

There is a school of thought that favours using a hard plastic surface rather

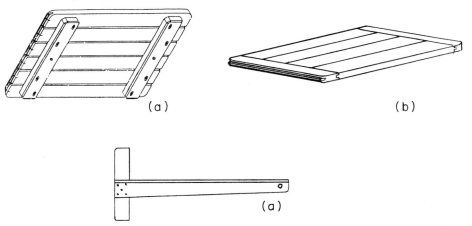

(a)   (b)

(a)

Fig. 70 *Drawing Boards. (a) battened type, viewed from below. (b) with "clamped" ends. Both have harder inserts at the working end. (c) typical tapered tee-square.*

than wood to work on. This doesn't matter very much, as you always need a backing sheet of stiff paper anyway, but it does mean that you must use draughting tape (a low-tack adhesive material) instead of drawing pins to hold down the paper. Now, drawing pins are 'old hat' these days - indeed, it is not easy to get the good quality type with large domed heads. But there are disadvantages to the use of tape. First, unless the paper is really good quality even the least tacky tapes will tear the surface. Worse still, it has a nasty habit of turning up an edge and sticking to the tee-square. Even when the board is used continuously it takes several years before the corners need attention when using pins, and these are probably the best for casual users.

Set squares (triangles in USA) are needed to draw lines at right angles to those done with the tee-square, and a pair, one at 45° and one 60° - 30°, is needed. They are sold from 3 inches up to 15 inches tall, but a pair about one-third of the width of the board is a good compromise. However, you may need to draw lines at other angles, and a single adjustable square can replace both. Mine (**Fig. 71**) are of celluloid, but most today are perspex. The same photo shows a very useful - indeed, indispensable - device, the erasing shield. That seen is of nickel silver, but most are of plastic. Placed over the drawing it enables you to rub out just part of a line without straying over the adjacent parts. (I haven't mentioned the eraser; an ordinary india-rubber will do, but it is best to spend a few pence more on a proper draughtsman's quality.)

If all your work is drawn full-size an ordinary ruler will serve provided that it is divided into thirty-seconds or 0.5mm, but a proper engineer's scale is otherwise essential. Two of mine are seen in **Fig. 71**, one covering full and half sizes on one side, with 1/4 and 1/8 on the back. The other scale is engraved in tenths and fiftieths of inches on one edge and in millimetres on the other. Those seen are posh, having xylonite edges, but plain boxwood is just as good. There are other scales to be had, but either of these will serve alone, depending on whether you work in imperial or metric.

You need to be able to draw circles, of course. You *can* get templates for this pur-pose - a lot of holes surrounded by perspex in calibrated sizes. Avoid them - they may be fair enough for artworkers, but are quite useless for precision work. You *must* have a pair of compasses. You can, of course, spend the earth on an elaborate cased set, but a single pair which will spread 4 inches, perhaps together with a lengthening bar, will serve. I would advise that you obtain a divider point that can be substituted for the pencil at the same time. All-important di-mensions should be picked up from the scale with dividers and transferred to the paper by 'pricking'. These can be expen-sive, but quite well engineered instruments can be bought for a few pounds. Cheap compasses, that spread their legs in use, are a waste of time and money. You may find difficulty in drawing small circles be-low about 6mm or 1/4 inch with these, and if you find you are spending a lot of time over them then look for a second-hand pair of spring bows. These have screw adjust-ment and can be set to very small radii with precision. Not essential, but highly desir-able as soon as you can afford them, see **Fig. 71(b)**. You may feel rather over-whelmed at this list, but most can be ob-

Fig. 71 *Adjustable and fixed set-squares; erasing shield;two 12in engineer's scales. (b) Compasses with extension; "Spring bow" compasses; Engineer's scales. (c) small clamped drawing board and tee-square with set squares of comparable size: traditional and "lead holder" pencils; and on the right, the author's pencil sharpening file.*

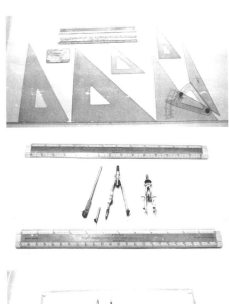

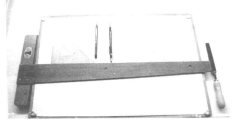

tained second-hand from local paper advertisements. I advise buying the set-squares new as these *must* be square to be effective (this doesn't matter with the tee-square so long as it is straight). **Fig. 72** shows two second-hand sets of instruments; the larger cost £3 and included three small set-squares. The smaller, a set of three very fine spring bows, cost £8 from an antiques fair. The former is a very good buy for anyone just starting up, while the spring bows were a collector's bargain, being very fine quality indeed. Good drawing instruments don't wear out; I am still using my set bought in 1929 - a complete outfit which cost £3-17s-6d

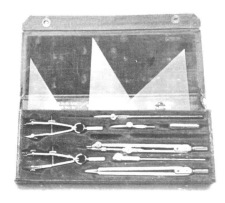

Laying out the drawing
You will need a backing sheet on the

Fig. 72 *Second-hand drawing instruments. The set on the right is more than adequate for the beginner.*

drawing-board first otherwise hard pencils will make grooves in the board. Thick cartridge paper, or a couple of sheets of ordinary drawing paper, will do. I use the backs of old and now redundant drawings.

If the drawing you are to make is small, you *can* use a correspondingly small sheet of paper, but I prefer to use the full size of the board - there will always be other drawings needed which can be set on the

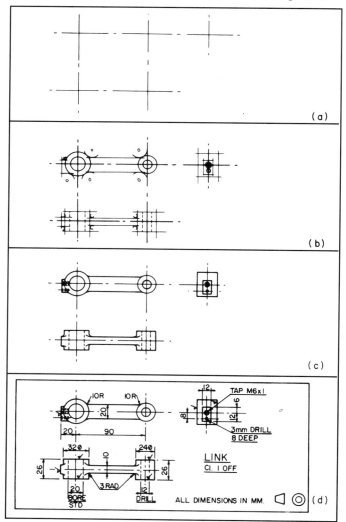

Fig. 73 *Successive steps in the making of a detail drawing.*

unused part. Pin or tape the top left-hand corner, draw the sheet tight towards the bottom right-hand corner and pin that; then the top right and finally the bottom left corners (reverse if you are left-handed). Now, if you are likely to take a fair time over the drawing (a day or so) then I recommend that you set the paper on the board the night before and retighten it before starting; paper does move with changes in weather. However, if the job will only take an hour or so this is not necessary. Make sure that your pencils are sharp and that your hands are clean - and the sleeves of whatever garment you are wearing

Start by estimating the amount of space you will need and how far apart the views will have to be. Trained draughtsmen will do this instinctively, but it pays to make a very rough sketch on some scrap paper. Now look at **Fig. 73**. We are going to make the drawing of the link seen at the bottom of the illustration. Start as at (**a**) by laying out, *very lightly,* the position of the centrelines. Use a hard pencil - 4H in my case - and exert no pressure. Let the bare weight of the pencil draw the lines. Compare this with your preliminary sketch, and check that you will be able to get in all the necessary views and their dimensions. Satisfied, proceed to step (**b**). Use a 3H pencil this time, but again, very lightly, to block in the outlines. Draw the large circles first, so that you can project the other views from them, and set out all other widths using dividers if you have them, or failing that, your compasses. Do not attempt to set out (e.g.) the width of the bosses or the shank by setting the scale rule across and using the point of your pencil. In fact, treat the setting out as you would a marking-out job in the workshop. Set out the radii for

the fillets with your compasses, and put a very faint ring round the spot where the compass points lie - the larger fillets, at least.

Check this and make sure that the various lines join up smoothly. Don't hesitate to rub out and redraw. The lines should be just visible and no more at this stage. The most common fault, with me at any rate, is to find that parallel lines are not *quite* equidistant from the appropriate centreline. Once satisfied you can then 'line in', as at (**c**). I used a 2H in making the illustration at this stage, although 3H would have served. You now know where the centres of the fillets should be, so, having drawn the larger circles next draw the fillets and marry the straight lines to them to get a clean outline. You can also add the hidden detail at this stage, though on a more complex drawing you should have indicated this at the earlier stage, (**b**).

The final step is to set out the dimension lines and dimensions, and finish off the drawing. Note that the various lines should be set out very lightly at first and not lined in until you are sure that you can get them all in and that the drawing will be clear. I used a 3H for the dimension lines and leaders, and H for the figures and letters, but you may find it easier with HB if you keep it really sharp. Add the machining marks, title and the symbol to show the type of projection used, put a border round the drawing, date it, and the job is done. There is no need to rub out the faint lines of stage (**b**).

This was a very simple example, of course, but it is exactly the procedure used for even the most complex drawing. On a sheet carrying a number of details you would, of course, treat each item as a separate drawing, following the **Fig. 73** procedure for each in turn. The object is to make a clear drawing, not crowded, but without having the views so far apart that they do not relate one to another. But it is not a bad rule to take *more* space than is really necessary rather than less. Clarity is the all-important objective.

Reproducing drawings

The prints used in an engineering workshop are made by using the drawings - traced in ink on film as a rule - as photographic negatives. In the old days these were blueprints, the paper being coated with a ferro-prussiate compound. This, when exposed to strong light (sunlight or arc light) and washed with water turns dark blue, the image of the lines on the tracing appearing white. Such prints last for ever and the only disadvantages are (a) that it is slow, and the wet prints must be dried and (b) many workshop fluids (including tea) bleach the blue to white. Unfortunately blue print paper is no longer available (though it is easily made) and modem prints appear as black or dark brown lines on a white background. This is

a dry process and prints can be used immediately they are made. The process does, however, need special equipment outside the means of most amateurs. With both processes it is possible to obtain fair prints from pencil drawings on tracing or detail paper (but not from thick cartridge paper) provided the lines are not too thin.

Plain paper copying services are now available in most towns. The latest plain paper copying machines use continuous paper of up to 1000mm width and have very fine resolution. A further advantage of even these very large machines is their ability to enlarge and reduce thus enabling quite large drawings produced full-size on the drawing board to be quickly and easily reduced to a convenient size for use in the workplace. A scan through the 'Reprographic Services' section of the 'Yellow Pages' will locate a suitable service. Of course, second-hand copiers do turn up from time to time, my own is one such and it has the advantage that it can reduce and enlarge; I can bring all prints down to A4 size, which is handy in the workshop.

Section 9

Reading Drawings

Anyone who has learned to write can, obviously, read. By now you should be able to make a reasonable drawing or sketch, and should, therefore be able to read them. However, there are difficulties occasionally. While a young child *can* read, it is not able to read fluently until much later, when he or she has had a lot of practice. That is the best advice I can give to start with. Make a lot of sketches and drawings, copying those from a magazine even, and use them in the shop. Stick exactly to the rules and grammar for every drawing you make, and especially correct any departures from the rules that you may find in published drawings.

Your biggest problem will be sorting out the type of projection used. It is most confusing when a book or magazine has no uniform practice and switches from first to third angle every few pages. It is criminally negligent when both styles are used on a single drawing - even worse when on the views of a single part. However, if you do come across such you can benefit indirectly, for the practice you get in *redrawing* the views in uniform projection is one of the most powerful aids to reading drawings. However, there is another aspect of the problem - that of visualisation. This is the reverse of the designer's task. He can 'see' the design object in his head, and all he has to do is to draw lines on paper to give a clear picture to others. These others, however, must work in reverse and 'see' the object just as the designer first imagined it. As I have already stated, practice is necessary. In **Fig. 26** you have already had a little exercise on this - although a very simple exercise if you achieved five out of six you are doing quite well. Now look at **Fig. 74**. These little sketches all have a line, sometimes two, missing from one of the views. Nevertheless, it is just possible to decide the shape of the object and hence to decide where these lines should be. Copy these sketches, one at a time, either as sketches, or better still, use your drawing-board and squares. Then make a pictorial sketch of the object and from this determine where the missing lines should go. Now, take care. I have cheated a little - *four* of the sketches are in third angle projection and the rest are in first angle, the natural projection. You must decide which they are and set the little

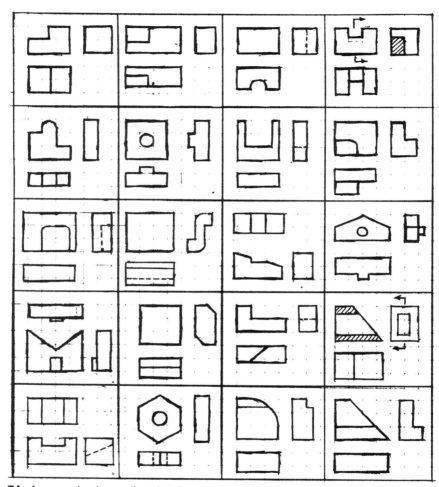

Fig. 74 *An exercise in reading drawings. Each sketch has one or two missing lines. Copy the sketches and see if you can find them. Warning; in all but the top row there is one sketch in third angle projection; all the rest are in first angle.*

symbol accordingly. However, to reduce your anxiety I will reveal that all the sketches in the first row are in first angle and that there is only one in third angle in each of the other rows. Note that some of the missing lines may be hidden detail - dotted lines. If you run into difficulties remember that if there is a line on the drawing there

84

will be line joining two points on the object, and that there must be a corresponding line on every view of the object. However, the line *may* appear as hidden detail, and if the line on the object would lie vertically on the paper, then it will appear only as a point. If you find yourself in real trouble over any of the sketches, make a little model out of Plasticine or balsa wood. This is quite a regular procedure; most engineers keep a stock of each in their offices.

In the case of published drawings, if you have any difficulty reading them, by far the best procedure is to make a new drawing. Even if it is no more than a straight copy of the original the very act of copying will help to clarify matters. But if there is much hidden detail in the form of dotted lines, then make *sectional* drawings of those parts. If you have no drawing tackle then make sketches on squared paper; it helps even if not exactly to scale. Note that this is not a confession of weakness. Such procedures are very common, especially in design offices, and unless things have changed a lot over recent years, patternmakers *always* copy complex drawings full size onto "scribing board". Imagine what the fully dimensioned drawing of the crankcase of the engine in **Fig. 75** would look like when it had eight cylinders - drawn at less than full size at that. I commend this procedure of redrawing to you; I use it a lot. If nothing else it may reveal the missing or erroneous dimensions, to say nothing of the odd missing line.

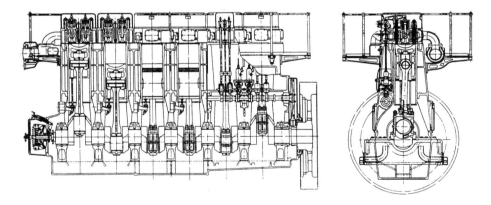

Fig. 75 *An assembly drawing of a "National" diesel engine, 16-1/2" bore x 21" stroke (From "Diesel Engine Design", T.D.Walshaw - Geo. Newnes, 1949)*

Section 10

Developments and Intersections

This is an aspect of workshop drawing that often arises when, for example, we need to cut out sheet metal which can be rolled into a specific shape, or when we need to cut a hole in a container - boiler or tank - which will be a close fit to a branching piece. A **development** is no more than the shape of the piece of sheet in the flat before folding and jointing. An intersection is the profile of the curve formed when two sections meet. You will find six of these on every nut where the cone of the chamfer meets the six flats. Normally we do not need to draw these accurately, but there can be occasions when this is necessary.

It is more than unfortunate that development drawings are usually a maze of lines. They can and do frighten off those not accustomed to them, and give the impression that this is very difficult; quite the wrong impression. Gypsy tinsmiths 100 years ago could lay out a development of (e.g.) a kettle spout almost in their sleep. And, of course, though there may be a maze of lines they are *all drawn one at a time,* and most will be a simple repetition of that drawn previously. but in a new place. However, there is an easy way to deal with

this problem. In each of the examples I am going to show toy how to do the job yourself as you read the page. Make a neat sketch of the object, and follow the instructions. Then, if you have time, get out the drawing-board and have a go on a similar problem of your own.

There can be scores of problems both for development and for intersection curves - indeed, there is at least one book on the subject dealing with nothing else. But the principle involved is the same in each case, and once you have mastered this you will be able to progress under your own steam to more elaborate systems should any come your way. But there is one matter which is quite vital, and which I must deal with first and that is the concept of the true length. Look at **Fig. 76**. Here we have a cone with a point 'X' on its side (it could be the corner of a hole). We want to mark this point on the flat sheet before we form the cone, so we need to know the length OX. However, looking at the elevation (the side view) we cannot scale the drawing because the line OX is sloping away from the eye; similarly, we cannot use the plan view, for the same reason. We can, of course, work

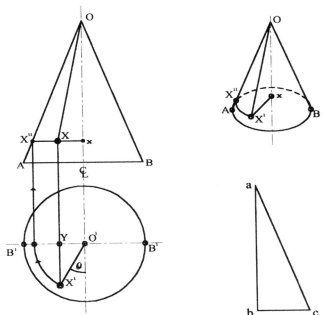

Fig. 76 *Finding the "true length" of an inclined line.*

it out very quickly, for the truly vertical distance, OX is one side of a right-angled triangle and the radial line in plan O'X', is its base. So we can draw the triangle I have shown as abc and either measure ac or work it out from $ac^2 = ab^2 + bc^2$. However, there is a simpler way. Look at the perspective sketch of the cone I have drawn. You will see that if we *rotate* the position of X about the vertical axis of the cone to the position X" then OX" gives the length we require. Looking back at the main drawing you will see that I have done just that; follow the arc from X' in the plan, then project upwards until we meet the side of the cone at X". Simple, isn't it? Simpler still when you notice that a line projected through X at right angles to the axis of the

cone also arrives at the right place. In most of what follows we shall be using this procedure, or some variant of it, no matter how complex it may seem. I am going to start with the cone, as this crops up very often indeed - for funnels in the shop and for lampshades in the house, too.

Development of a cone (Fig. 77)

First a few definitions. The *vertical height* is that measured along the axis or centreline. The *slant height* is that measured along the sloping side. The *cone angle* is the angle included at the peak of the cone, and the *developed angle* is that made at the peak of the sheet in the flat. The *base diameter* is the diameter of the complete cone; we shall, shortly, be dealing

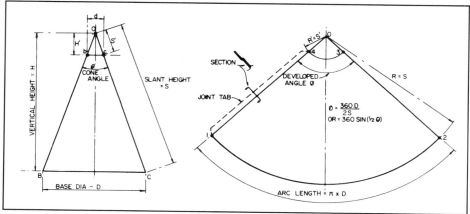

Fig. 77 *The development of a cone onto a flat sheet.*

with the case where the cone is cut off at an angle.

The development is a very simple one, forming, as you see, a fan shape. In the drawing I have supposed that we are making a funnel, so that we need a hole in the top of diameter 'd'. It needs little abstruse mathematics to see that the length of the *side* of the fan must be S-s' - the difference between the slant height of the main cone and the little cone we do not want. It is also clear that the length of the arc at the extremity of the fan must be equal to the circumference of the cone base diameter, which will be πD (π= 22/7 or 3.14 for this sort of work). However, this is not easy to lay out, and it is easier to work out the developed angle. I have given the formula on the drawing. The upper one is the easier to use, and if you don't know what the slant height 'S' is you can either work it out from $S^2 = H^2 + (1/2\ D\ )^2$ (but note the 'S' must be taken from the vertex 'O') or you can measure it. I always draw these developments to as large a scale as I can

and measure from the drawing.

You will, of course, require a small overlap to make the joint - I have shown a suggestion on the drawing. Although this is not a treatise on how to make cones, if you do need one with a true point then I suggest the method shown in Fig. 78. It is

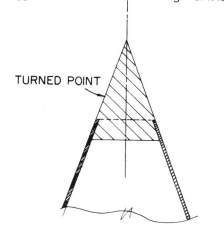

Fig. 78 *Forming the point at the vertex of a cone.*

quite impossible to fold even thin sheet metal to an exact point. Now try one for yourself - make it in stiff card or even paper if you have no use for a tin funnel.

The sliced-off cone

The proper name for this is a frustum (**Fig. 79**), this being Latin for 'a part' or 'cut off. (Latin because the method was worked out over 2000 years ago.) At first sight it looks formidable, but remember what I said; the lines are drawn one after the other, in a system. To make the example universal I have sliced off both the top and the bottom at different angles, along BD and EF. You will see that the 'fan' is now a very odd shape indeed, but in fact, all we need are the true lengths of the lines radiating from the apex of the cone. I have marked one of

these as D'F', and shown it on the fan.

In this case I suggest that you make a proper elevation drawing of the 'frustrated' cone and its plan view, but you can manage with a sketch if you are careful. Just the outline at present; never mind all the construction lines. Then proceed as follows, remembering that the object is to determine the true lengths between the slices all round the cone.

(1) Divide the plan view into equal parts, I have shown 12. More would be better, but it is seldom necessary to go beyond 16, easy with a 45deg. set-square. But work as accurately as you can in setting out.

(2) Number the radials 1 to 12 as I have shown. This makes it easier to follow.(3)

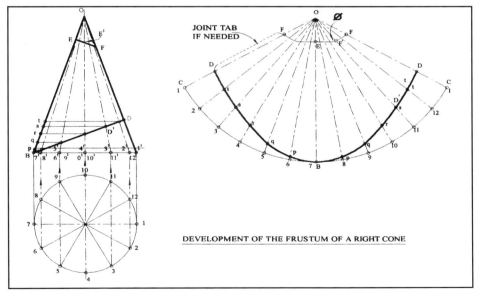

DEVELOPMENT OF THE FRUSTUM OF A RIGHT CONE

Fig.79 *Development of a "frustum" of a cone.*

89

Project vertical lines from the points on the circle to meet the base of the cone. I have shown these points as 1', 2', 3' etc. *Note:* You will notice immediately that there is no need for a complete plan view; a semi-circle would suffice, as the points 8' to 12' lie on top of those from 6' to 2'. This is true for all developments which are, like this cone, symmetrical.

(4) Draw lines from the points on the base (1', 2' etc.) to the apex of the cone. Mark where they cross the planes of section, BD and EF.

(5) Project horizontally from these intersection points to meet the slant side of the cone. (I have marked these as p,q,r,s,t.) I have *not* marked these on the plane EF, do that for yourself.

(6) Draw the fan as if the cone were intact, using the method already described in **Fig. 77**. Set out radial lines as shown, by dividing the projected angle 0 by the number of divisions you have used on the plan - 12 in this case. Number each of these radial lines to correspond with the numbers on the plan view.

(7) Working from the base (BC) upwards, set off the distance CD from the elevation onto the end radials of the fan.

(8) Similarly set off the distance Bp from the elevation on the fan at the radial corresponding to points 6 and 8.

(9) Set off, in turn, Bq, Br, Bs and Bt on the fan to correspond with radials 5/9, 4/10, 3/11 and 1/12.

(l0) Join the points on the fan radials with a

smooth curve.

(11) Repeat this procedure for the upper slice, EF, this time measuring lengths from the *apex* of the cone.

Again, you will need a jointing tab (unless you are going to make a butt-brazed joint) but this is a matter of workshop practice, not drawing.

Try this fellow with a sheet of thin tinplate or card and see how you get on. It is really very easy once you take your courage in both hands and have a go. However, there is one point of detail worth mentioning. I usually do these developments full size on either thin tinplate or on tinsmith's template paper - a fairly stiff paper-like material which takes pencil and yet will withstand hard usage in the shop. After a trial to see that all is well I

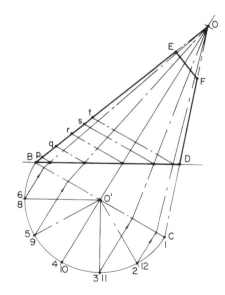

Fig. 80 *The inclined circular cone. This is, in effect, the same as Fig. 79.*

then use this as a template to mark out the actual workpiece. However, if the development is very important or complicated, then I draw the diagrams either twice or five times full size, take dimensions off and reduce them to the actual workpiece. You *must* use very sharp pencils and take care over the setting out when an actual workpiece is involved though sketches may be quite adequate if you are just practising draughtsmanship.

The inclined cone (Fig. 80)

This looks like a new shape but it is, in fact, identical to that in **Fig. 79**, and can be treated as such. You can do the construction either with the centreline of the cone vertical, or in the design position, **Fig. 80**.The former is more convenient if all you need is the development, but the latter makes it easier to carry out the next stage. Before coming to that, however, I show in **Fig. 81** an application of this conic section which you might think worth making; a funnel I made many years ago for feeding a car from a jerrican. I find it very useful

with modern cars.

Base of the inclined cone (Fig. 82)

We may need to know the shape of the cutting plane across BD - the base of the cone as drawn. This may look very formidable but, again, the lines are drawn one by one, and much of what you see on **Fig. 82** you have done already. In fact, you proceed exactly as you would to prepare the development, but do it with the cone on the slant. This finds the points p,q,r,s,t, but notice that I have added points at p',q',r',s' and t' on the true centreline of the cone. Now proceed as follows.

(I) Draw a line parallel to BD some convenient distance below.

(2) From the numbered points on BD drop perpendiculars to this line; these I have marked with double arrows. (The lines with single arrows are drawn as for the construction of a development.)

(3) Set compasses to a radius equal to t-t' and, on the plan at X' scribe an arc which crosses the radial lines 2 and 12. (Note that these radials correspond to the lines used in *finding* the point)

(4) Set compasses to radius s-s' and draw an arc to cross the radials 3 and 11 .The same comment applies.

(5) Repeat this process for radii equal to r-r', q-q' and p-p' in turn, crossing radials 4-10, 5-9 and 6-8.

(6) Draw lines joining these intersections between arcs and radials, and set identification numbers against them - look

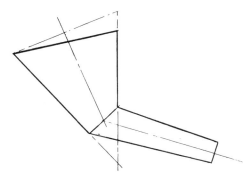

Fig. 81 *One application of a conic frustum.*

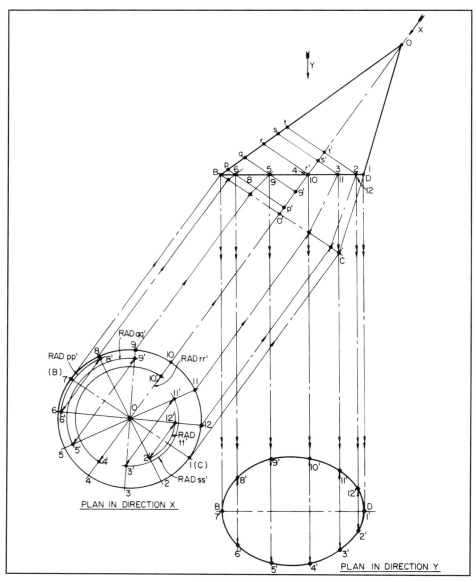

Fig. 82 *Developing the plan shape of the inclined cone.*

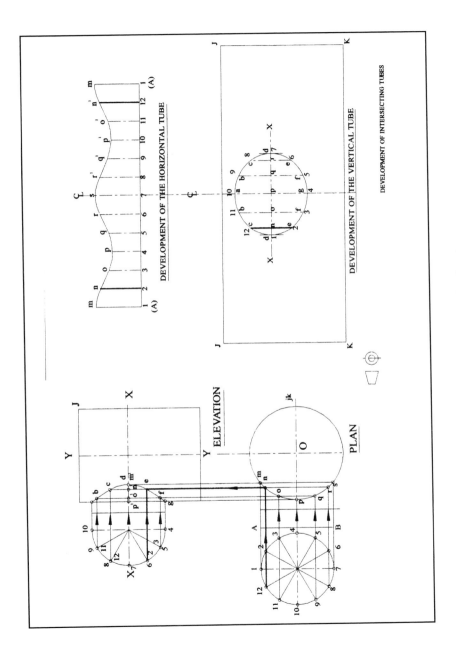

Fig. 83 *Intersection of circular ducts. One line of the construction has been emboldened to make it easier to follow.*

93

at my drawing. *The lengths of these lines are equal to the width of the base (i.e. measured vertical to the plane of the paper) at the corresponding points on BD.*

(7) Set out these lengths on the 'plan in direction Y' as shown on the drawing. Draw a smooth curve through the points so found, giving the outline of the shape.

This may seem to be complicated, but if you have followed the steps you should have had no problems. If you *haven't* done so, do it now, for while it is easy to forget what you have read, that which you have *done* will stick in your mind. However, if you look back to **Fig. 76** you will see that all we have done is the reverse of that procedure. Imagine the cone sliced off along AX. We look *down* the cone axis while we move from X" to X, so that this movement is a true arc. Then the distance X'-y in **Fig. 76** *must* be half the width of the sliced-off part at this point. We then look down again, but this time normal to the base of the inclined cone (i.e. along the arrow Y in **Fig. 82**) to plot this as a true length on the plan view. The *only* difficulty with these development and intersection curves lies in deciding from which direction to view the solid in order to see the true length.

Intersecting cylinders

This is a very common case, where pipes or tubes of differing diameters meet. We will deal with the simple case of tubes at right angles first. We start by drawing the elevation and plan to scale, but leave space on the paper for the development, the length of which will be the circumference of the larger tube. Draw circles centred on the side tube centrelines, as you see. However, note that I have used only a semi-circle on the elevation. There

is, in fact no need for a full circle in any of the constructions done so far; I have used them only to make the projections a bit clearer. Stick to the full circle on the plan in this case as well, until you get used to the drill. Divide the circles, as before, into sectors.

Now, observe: the figure 10 on the elevation lies at the *top* - at 1200 hrs. This means that it is on the centreline of the assembly. In the plan, therefore, it must also be on the centreline i.e. at 0900 hrs. The figure 7 is at the front - visible in the elevation - and I have marked it *outside* the circle on the elevation. Figure 1, however, is at the back, invisible in elevation, and is marked *inside* the circle. In this particular case these distinctions do not matter, but they often do, and it is important to be able to distinguish between these falsely similar positions. Now proceed as follows:

(1) From the intersections between radials and the circumference of *both* circles draw horizontal lines. They should reach far enough to pass the points 'm' and 's', already identified in the plan view.

(2) Look at the plan view. Identify the intersection of each of these horizontal projections with the circumference of the vertical tube (a circle seen in plan) and mark it with a letter. I have used m to s.

(3) From each of these points draw a vertical line to meet the horizontal line from the corresponding point on the elevation's circle thus 6-r-e-6, or 8-r-e-8. You must take care to *identify* the points and lines 'back' or 'front'. In this case they lie one above the other, but this is not necessarily so, if,

for example, the tubes do not have a common centreline.

(4) Mark these intersections as I have done, using letters a to g. Draw a smooth curve through these points. This is the *true shape* of the intersection when seen in elevation.

Now to draw the developments, needed if the joint were to be made from sheet metal. Let us do the small tube first.

(1) Draw a horizontal line ABA, equal in length to the circumference of the small tube, and divide it into the same number of equal parts as there are radials on your circles. Number these to correspond. *Note* that I have started at point '1' - this means that the joint will be there when it is fabricated. Adjust the numbering to bring the joint where you need it.

(2) Draw vertical lines at each of the numbered points, a little longer than the length A-m in the plan view, and add the identifying letter to correspond with each of the numbers. *Note* that these letters will repeat in mirror fashion; I have used a dashed letter (e.g. p') to identify letters corresponding to the numbers 8 to 12.

(3) Set your dividers to the length A-m in the plan and step this off at 1, 7 and 1 again on the development. (Bs = Am in this example.)

(4) Repeat this procedure for lengths from n, o, p. q, r to the line AB, setting each in turn at its proper place on the development.

(5) Draw a smooth curve through the points so determined. This gives the profile to which the sheet must be cut to make a smooth joint to the intersection. (Don't forget to leave on a tab at one end if you are using a lap joint.)

Just a point of detail. It is prudent to arrange the joint *exactly* on one of the ordinates you have constructed, as if you set it elsewhere and perhaps make a slight error the stub will not point in the desired direction. I usually make my joints on one of the two centrelines, then it is easier to line up accurately.

Now for the hole in the large pipe. Set out the centreline and draw the rectangle, length equal to the circumference and height equal to the distance JK. Draw the horizontal centreline shown as XX. We now have to space out the vertical lines you see, which correspond to the lines bf, ce etc. on the elevation. These *ought* to be spaced by measuring along the *circumference* of the cylinder between (e.g.) o and p. This is not easy, but if you work it out you will find that the error arising from measuring the chord is very small. With a 3 inch branch and 4 inch main the error on pq is about 0.007 inches. It would be much less if we had used 16 radials instead of 12. Moreover, the error on the other spacings will be even less. This being so we can use the chords, but 'measure full' when transferring the dimensions. Proceed as follows.

(1) Set dividers to the chord op (which is the same as pq) and set off on either side of the centreline of the development. Draw the two vertical lines 3-11 and 5-9.

(2)Repeat, stepping off the chord no (or qr), set these out on the XX line of the development spacing from the points already marked. Repeat again with the chords nm/rs. You will now have five vertical lines - the two end points are, of course, just points.

(3) Refer to the elevation of the joint. You will see that the height of the hole at p in the plan must be the diameter of the branch. Set this out on the development. (I have marked this ag in letters and 10-4 in figures, to correspond to the elevation.)

(4) Measure from the centreline at o' to b (note that o'b = o'O and set this dimension on the appropriate vertical in the development. Note that this will also provide the heights for the vertical line 5-9.

(5) Repeat for n'c, completing lines 2-12 and 6-8 on the development.
There is no need to measure full for these vertical lines; they will be as correct as your draughtsmanship allows. A smooth curve drawn through the points gives the shape of the required opening.

Now, the more observant reader will have noticed that I have made a fair amount of extra work for myself - and for you - in all this measuring. In fact, I have done it on purpose, but never mind that. The point is that if I had set the centreline XX of the last development in line with the centreline XX on the elevation, I could have projected the heights we transferred with dividers. Similarly, if I had set the development of the branch below the plan, with the line ABA aligned to AB on the branch, I could have projected the heights here also, though the development would have 'stood on end' as it were. The reason is that circumstances can arise where direct projection is not possible - or would be very difficult -so that

dimension transfer with dividers has to be resorted to.

Now, if you have forgotten what I said at the beginning and have simply tried to follow the instructions by reading, get out your paper and pencil and *do it for yourself* It is the only way to learn, and you will (I hope) be agreeably surprised to find how easy it is. To make it easier to follow I have emphasised one corresponding set of projection lines and the resulting lines on the developments.

The inclined and offset junction
By now you have had some experience, so that I have no hesitation in dealing with two elaborations at once. This time there is some justification for projecting by measurement. The development of the hole in the vertical tube could be projected easily enough, but that for the inclined branch would have to be laid out on an extension of the left-hand side of the paper; we must view the true lengths and this could only be done by looking in the direction of the arrow 'P'. Draw the outlines of the elevation and plan, leaving the end of the branch in plan blank for the time being - this must be constructed. In doing so, note that the *position* of such a branch may be defined from the centrelines, by the dimension DE, *or* at the surface of the main pipe, by dimension OF. As it is offset, the preferred way is to use the two dimensions DE and (in plan) CD. This does not affect the constructions, but is important in the design stage. Note that in plan the lengths of the side stub will not be *true* lengths, though *the widths* will be true. Further, as the stub is offset the shape of the intersection and the development will not be the same at the front as at the back.

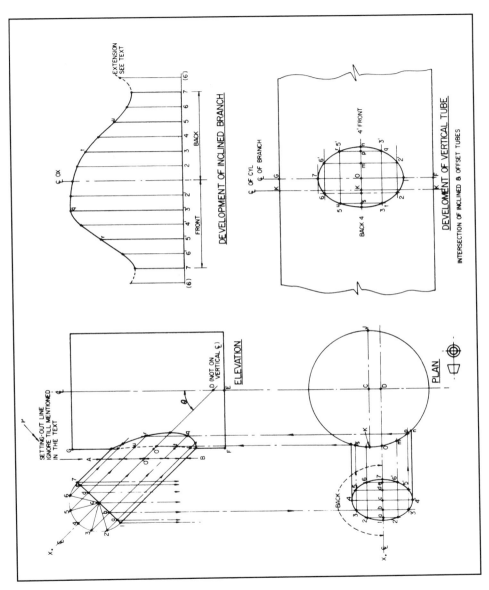

Fig. 84 *The intersection of inclined and offset cylinders.*

97

You must take care to identify front and back points as you go along. Finally, American readers please note that this example, like all the others, is executed in *first angle projection*. In this one it makes quite a difference to procedure if you wish to use third angle, as everything must be reversed. Stick to first angle.

As this example needs more construction lines than usual I am not going to draw all of them, but just 'talk you through' one or two; you can then repeat the process for the others. I do emphasise that with this example in particular you will be most ill-advised if you try to follow the procedure just by reading the page; get out the drawing-board and do each step (and the repetitions) as it arises.

The first thing we have to do is to obtain the shape in plan of the end of the branch. On the elevation, set out a circle - I have used a semi-circle, as it is symmetrical - on the end of the branch and divide it into segments. Draw the radial lines and insert the identification numbers and letters. Drop perpendicular projection lines down to the plan from points 1 and 7. These define the extreme points on this view. Do the same for the other points a.b.c.d.e; I have shown that from 'b' only. Mark the letters on the stub centreline XD on the plan as I have done.

Take the case of line 'b' to see how to determine the widths in plan. Measure the length b-3 in the elevation semicircle and set this dimension either side of 'b' in plan to obtain the two points 3 and 3'. Do this for all the other points, noting that the lengths b-3 and d-5 are the same as are a-2 and e-6. This done, draw a smooth curve through the points. I recommend that you now draw a dotted curve as I have done,

boldly marked BACK, just to remind you which is back and front.

The next job is to determine the shape of the *intersection curves* on the *elevation*. The drill is:

(1) Draw projection lines parallel to the axis of the branch from the points 1-2-3-4 etc. at the ends of the radials, long enough to reach into the vertical cylinder.

(2) Draw projection lines from the points 1-2-3-4- etc. on the plan of the end of the branch to meet the circumference of the vertical cylinder. Identify the points of intersection with letters.

(3) Draw vertical projection lines from the lettered points in plan to meet the corresponding points on the parallels in the elevation.
I have drawn in two. From 3-5 in plan to 's'. From the intersection at s' vertically to meet the line from 3 at 't' and from 5 at 'u'. Again, from 3'-5' to 'p'; vertically to meet the parallel from 3' (the same line as from 3) at 'q', and from the radial 5' (same as from *5)* at 'r'. These are at the *front* on the elevation, and I have ringed these points; those at the *back* are plain dots.

(4) Once all vertical projection lines have been drawn the outline of the intersection can be drawn. Full line at the front, and dotted line at the back.

Now for the *development of the branch*. The procedure is as already described. Draw the base line and mark out the divisions sideways from the centreline. Note that there is an extra one at each end - this makes it easier to draw the final curve. The heights of the ordinates are measured on the *elevation* from the line a-b-c-d- etc.

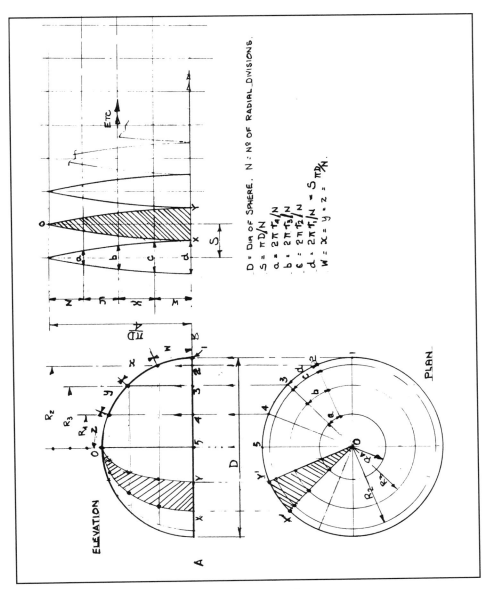

Fig. 85 *Approximate development of a spherical surface.*

99

to the curves q-r- and t-u-, and you will see that I have marked these four on the developments. Take care in identifying front and back. Note also that the curve does change curvature rather rapidly in places. This is a case where it would have been prudent to use more radials, say 16 rather than 12.

The development of the *hole* in the main cylinder does need more care, and the use of a trick. Set out the horizontal centreline, which will, in the elevation, be a circumferential line through 'O'. Now, if the branch has been located by the dimension DE in elevation you must ascertain the length OF on the circumference. You can do this by measurement if the drawing is carefully made; or you can calculate it, from OF = FE.Tan O + DE. (EF is the radius of the cylinder.) Then draw the baseline and from this measure up a distance FG to get the position of the top line.

Now *take great care* and set off the distance OK; make sure that you get it on the correct side, the drawing is *in first angle* projection. Then proceed as follows:

(1) Use your dividers to set out the distances Om, mp, pn from the plan view (measured on the circumference of the vertical cylinder) onto the development to the *right* of the point '0'.

(2) Repeat this, procedure for the points on the left of 'O'. *Note* that these distances are **not** symmetrical about O; they must be measured individually.

(3) On the elevation draw the vertical line AB at some convenient point. (This line is used to measure the *vertical* ordinates, which might be difficult along the line tu otherwise).

(4) Measure the vertical distance from 0' to the line btq and set this on the development. Make dots where this line crosses the vertical lines marked 's' and 'p'. (These are the corresponding points in the plan view.)

(5) Repeat for all the other points on the development and draw a smooth curve through them.

Note that though this development may *look* like a perfect ellipse this is not the case. The hole is not symmetrical about the centreline GOF.

This construction will serve for any angle of inclination or degree of offset; if 0 is 90° then you have a simple right-angled tee which is offset, and if the offset is zero then the plan view is symmetrical. Such cases are less work, that is all. However, there is just one point of geometry that needs watching. If the angle is less than about 45°, or if the offset is such that the branch lies entirely to one side of the larger cylinder's centreline, then it is almost essential to use more ordinates on the originating circle on the branch, 16 at least, and at the critical points even these may need to be divided again.

There is, by the way, no geometrical reason for equal divisions; you can place them as you wish. We use equal divisions only because they are easier to set out.

Development of a sphere

No surface which curves in two or more planes can be developed truly from the flat, but it is possible to make a reasonable approximation. **Fig. 85** shows the treatment of a hemisphere. Those of you who have seen geographical globes will have noticed that the map is cut up into slices rather like the segments of an orange; these are known as gores, and their construction is not at all difficult. In fact, it is possible to achieve a reasonable spherical shape with very little construction indeed.

Draw the plan and elevation, and divide the plan into sectors with radial lines. In this case you do need closer intervals, and 16 radials is the minimum. As before, identity each radial with a number. Project from the intersection of radials and circumference vertically upwards to meet the base AB and continue upwards to meet the outline of the sphere in elevation. Set your compass to the radii shown as R_2, R_3, R_4 in the elevation. (R_1 is the radius of the sphere, D/2.) Describe arcs on the plan using these radii. Identify (i) the lengths of the arcs between adjacent radials, shown as a, b, c, d; and (ii) the lengths of the corresponding arcs on the elevation, shown as w, x, y, z.

Now, look at the plan. You will see that a sector has been shaded. This is the plan view of one of the gores. Project upwards from the points of intersection of radials and circles (shown with dots) and you get the shape OXY seen in elevation. To prepare the *development* first set out a base line equal in length to the circumference of the sphere. Divide this into as many equal parts as you have segments in plan. You will see that I have shown one shaded, and XY corresponds to X'Y' on the plan. Draw a parallel line above the base, distance away equal to one quarter of the circumference, and further parallels at distances w, x, y, and z apart. (These distances will be equal, and should add up to the quarter-circumference.) On these lines set out the widths a, b, c, d as shown. Then draw

smooth curves through the points so found to form the gores. There will, of course, be as many of these as there are sectors between the radials. This is not a difficult construction, and can, of course, be adapted. The back of a bend, for example, can be developed simply by halving the number of gores - making a quarter sphere. However, it can be much easier than that. On the drawing I have given the necessary algebra (trigonometry?) needed to *calculate* the various dimensions required to construct the chain of gores. There is no need to draw it out at all. Finally, for a 'rough job' advantage can be taken of the fact that the profile of the gores approximates to the arc of a circle. It is only necessary to set out the three points X, Y, and 0 and, by trial, strike an arc which is centred on the base line and passes through 0 and Y. In any case, it is not necessary to construct a row of gores. You can mark out one on a sheet of tinplate or brass, file to shape, and use it as a template.

Practical points

This is not a book on sheet metal work, but it may be advisable to mention two points. First; developments for work in thin sheet can be constructed and used as drawn. However, if the metal has any appreciable thickness - more than, say 2% of the diameter of the object - you will be well advised to allow for this. Each case must be considered individually, but in general you will not go far wrong if you make your initial drawing to dimensions which correspond to the mid thickness of the work. For example, for a cylinder 4 inch dia x 1/8 inch thick, make the drawing for 3-7/8 inch diameter.

In the case of a sphere the workpiece

101

will braze up with a series of flat segments. You can ease this by doing a bit of panel beating on the segments to form a slight lateral curvature. Further, when making such a hemisphere, for a dome cover or similar, I use the technique applied to the cone in **Fig. 78**. Turn up a little disc with a spherical top, a ridge on which the ends of the gore can sit, and then file or machine all flush after brazing.

Conclusion

You may well come across even more elaborate cases, especially if you ever see any examination papers in so-called 'engineering' drawing. Academic examiners get high on things like 'ellipsoidal cones intersecting hypertrochoidal solids of revolution'. However, if you have followed me so far you have mastered sufficient of the art of development to cover most practical cases that arise in the ordinary workshop. If anything odd does turn up just remember that you need the *true length*. Draw an arrow showing the direction from which you will 'see' the true length, and then arrange your construction so that the views are seen from the direction of the arrow or arrows if more than one.

Finally, you may now appreciate why the college courses always start with this sort of construction. Once you have done a couple of developments you should have no difficulty at all in projecting one view of a pair of inside cylinders from another.

Section 11

Metric and Imperial Drawings

The translation of a metric drawing to imperial dimensions presents little difficulty, as the amended dimensions would be in decimal inches, and these would imply the same degree of precision as on the original; thus 26mm could translate as 1", or as 1.02" or depending on the class of work. Translating from inches to mm differs, however, as many designers still use fractional dimension rather than decimals, and some even work in sixty-fourths. If such fractional dimensions are toleranced the degree of precision is indicated. Even so, the fraction itself may imply working in tenths of thous - 13/16" ± 0.001" means 0.8115" to 0.8135", which converts to 20.612mm to 20.663mm. In the same situation a metric designer would probably write 20.50 to

20.5 5mm - a tolerance of ± 0.025mm. The situation is aggravated in drawings of any age, often untoleranced, and even more so on drawings prepared for modelmakers, where the user is expected to relate the dimensions of mating parts and so establish the degree of precision required.

The first step is to go systematically over the whole drawing, converting every dimension to the opposite system. I recommend that figures in inches be taken to 4 places of decimals, or if converting to metric, to three; these can be refined later. Next, seek out and identify the two opposite extremes of precision needed. FIRST, those that must tally with a bought-in component e.g. a ballrace or the bore of a gearwheel which you cannot alter. Mark these plainly and, I suggest, make a note of them. SECOND, mark up figures which are clearly rule dimensions; usually unmachined surfaces, spacing of holding-down bolt-holes and so on.

It is then wise to lay a rule over the castings to assess the amount of machining allowance you have to play with. Note this, in both systems of measurement. You should then identify matching dimensions of the less critical kind where, within the limits of the machining allowance, you can alter the dimension of both mating parts to a round number (e.g. a 15/16" dia spigot (23.81mm) could be probably be made 24mm -or even 25mm - with no problem). The point here, as with the ruler dimensions, is to select conversions that are easy to measure in the opposite system, whether by calipers or with the micrometer or vernier.

The next step is more important. That is to establish reference faces and centrelines so that working parts will align. The point is easily appreciated; dimensions in fractional inches will seldom convert to round hundredths of millimeters - the smallest increment that you can work with a normal micrometer. The throw of a crankshaft, for example, or the location of an eccentric relative to the valve-chest, must be dimensioned to an exact match. This must be done carefully and, I suggest, the revised dimensions entered on the drawing as you proceed. Having checked them you can then fill in any remaining dimensions - it is quite certain that some of those previously determined will have to be altered.

My own practice at this stage is to make a new drawing altogether, filling in the metric dimensions (or inch, if I am converting from Metric) as I would were I doing the job from scratch. But there is, in these days of accessible copiers, a very useful aid. Make a copy of the original drawing and go over this deleting all the dimensions with liquid paper (e.g. *Tippex*). Then get copies made of this undimensioned drawing. You can then enter on one copy the literal conversions you made at the beginning, as well as the reference faces and centrelines. The second copy can then be used for the various steps mentioned, and the third used for entering your final decisions.

I have shown the process on a relatively simple example. This (**Fig. 86**) is the crankcase, crankshaft and bearing housing for a small two-cylinder single acting high-speed steam engine for a model

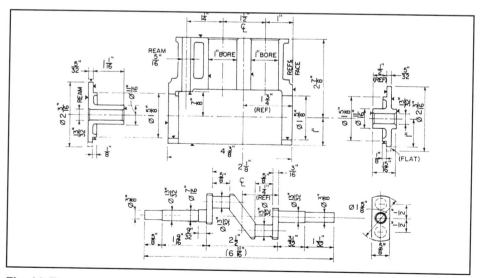

Fig. 86 *The original "imperial" drawing prior to metrication.*

104

boat. I have not shown all the details as by the time the drawing is reduced to book size it would have been smothered in figures. (Most of the omitted detail is concerned with stud positions, oil-holes and the like, which present few problems.) **Fig. 86** is the original inch drawing and you will see that I have added reference details; the centrelines of the block and crank, and the length 1/2 inch) of the boss on the right-hand bearing housing, which locates the crank endways. It is, of course, obvious that the spacing of the two crankpins must align with the spacing of the cylinder bores. I have also added machining marks - often absent from drawings published for use by modelmakers, unfortunately.

Before going further there is one decision which had to be made, that of the cylinder bore (and, perhaps, the stroke). A metric design of engine would have a bore of 25mm, not *25.4mm,* and if 25mm piston rings were available this is the proper conversion. In this case, however, the piston rings were to hand for a bore of 1.000 inch; to reduce the bore to 25mm would mean filing at the gap, removing 1.26mm (about 0.050") and though this presents no difficulty there would be a risk that the ring might not fit properly. So, the decision is made to keep to 1" or 25.4mm and as there is no difficulty with the crank either, the throw is retained at the metric equivalent of 1/2 inch - 12.7mm.

Fig. 87 shows a second copy of the drawing dimensioned with exact metric conversions, though all have been rounded off to the third decimal place. You will notice a number of dimensions marked with an asterisk *; these are all rule dimensions, which can be altered within the limits of the machining allowance (3/32 inch or 2.4mm)

to suit the machinist's convenience. We have one dimension (apart from the cylinder bore) which must fit a bought-in part; the 7/16 in. dia on the shaft, marked A, carries a commercial bevel gear. Compare Fig. 86 with Fig. 87, and you will see that it is dimensioned at 11.11mm (0.437in.). The machinist can work to either, the difference between the two being 0.003mm or 0.00001", not significant. There are some places where parts can be machined to a mutual fit, marked B. The end bearing housings, both the spigot and the bearing bore; the mating part of the shaft; the ends of the shaft, which fit to flywheel and coupling; and the vertical reamed hole which carries the bevel-wheel shaft. Consider these in turn. The spigot can be 42mm, not critical provided the crank can be passed through. The shaft bearing can be 10mm, a standard reamer size; a little homework shows that the combined bending and torsion stress will still be reasonable. The shaft ends can be 9mm with no harm, still standard reamer size, and the vertical shaft 8mm. Now consider the dimension C - the height of the block above the crank centreline. This dimension would affect the piston clearance at dead centre. Examination of the connecting rod forging showed that centres had to be held fairly close. The exact 73.025 is, therefore, held at 73mm, instead of being altered to 75 which would be a more normal dimension here.

Now for the critical part - aligning crank and block. Compare Figs 86 and 87 during the next stages. The cylinder centre distance, D can be refined to 38mm, and that from the centre of bore No. 1 to the reference face made 26mm without over-running the machining allowance - D_1. (We

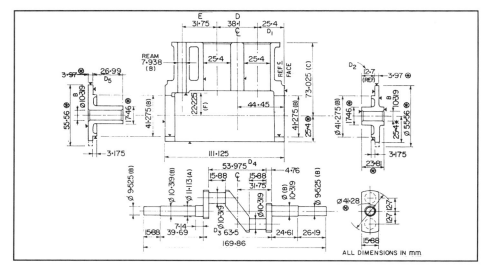

Fig. 87 *In this intermediate stage, all dimmensions have been converted to metric but to three places of decimals.*

increase D_1, as a little, as we decreased D.) This brings the reference dimension, originally 44.45mm, to 45mm. Again, a convenient round figure. Turn to the crankshaft. The outer faces of the two webs determine the shaft location, D3. Make this 64mm for trial. Then, if the crankpins are made 16mm wide (the big end bearing can be machined to suit) and the webs made 5mm thick the centre distance of the two crankpins works out at 38mm, exactly as required for the cylinder bores. It only remains to adjust the length of the location boss on the right-hand end plate to match up (D_2) and this works out at 13mm. To summarise, we find D at 38, D_1, at 26, D_2 at 13, D_3 at 64, and crankpin width at 16mm. The only remaining dimension of this group is D_5, the boss on the left-hand end cover. This has been set at 28mm (not 27) to allow

the overall length of the block to be rounded to 112mm. Some adjustment will be needed at erection in any case, to allow for setting the meshing of the bevel gears.

Apart from details of rule dimensions the only remaining items to be settled are, first, the crankpin diameter and secondly, the dimensions marked E and F. The crankpins can be either 10mm or 11mm, both standard reamer sizes. If 10mm, the stress will go up by about 9% - well within the safe limit for drop-forged steel - and I would use that figure, if only to avoid yet another reamer size. However, those who have an eye to increasing bearing life would certainly plump for 11mm dia here. The lengths of the various steps in the shaft are not at all critical, and would be simply rounded from the exact figures.

Now for E and F. The figure at E can

106

affect the valve timing, (the engine has a transverse piston valve operated by a link from the vertical shaft). Slight adjustment is possible. The exact dimension from the block centreline is 2 inches = 50.8mm. If E is made 32mm, this dimension becomes 51mm, a difference of 0.2mm, about 0.008 inch. But we have, as it happens, moved the seating of the bevel gear on the shaft endways by 0.25mm, which compensates almost exactly. So, E can be 32mm with no problems. Finally, F. This figure affects the meshing of the two bevels. The distance is, therefore, rounded **upwards,** so that shim-washers can be used for adjustment. In all this work it will be helpful to remember that 0.1mm is almost four thou

(0.004") and 0.01mm four-tenths. For the metric user, one thou (0.001") is 0.025mm when converting drawings in the opposite direction.

References between Figs 86 and 87 will show how the other, minor, dimensions have been settled and you will notice that we have been able to make the final conversion in round figures of millimetres with very few exceptions. We have, in effect, redesigned the four components to S.I. standards.

Agreed, this exercise has taken some time, and to deal with all the lesser dimensions not shown on the sketches - **and** those on the two or three score other parts - would take even longer. As I said

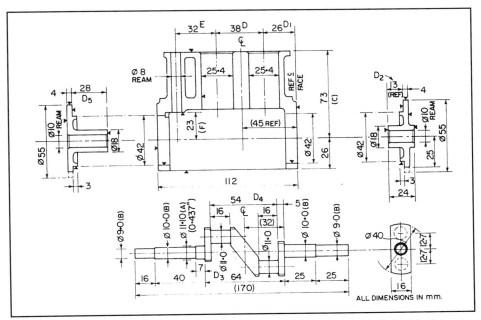

Fig. 88 *The fully metric drawing. Note that the cylinder bore and crankshaft ballrace sizes remain at exact metric conversions.*

107

before, we are really redesigning the engine with the constraint of having to work to the existing castings, and this, inevitably, takes longer than designing an engine and leaving the materials supplier to make patterns and castings for you.

On a really large set of drawings, of course, the job would be formidable indeed, and some would say that it was impossible. This is far from being the case. It is, in fact easier than reducing the prototype from full size to model scale; at 1 in/ft 19 inches comes out at 1.583333 in. However, it does take time, and I find that by far the best procedure when a number of really large drawings are involved is, after carrying out the initial steps (identifying rule, mating, and exact dimensions, and then making an exact conversion of all) to get out the drawing-board and make a new set of drawings altogether. I would add a further piece of advice, too. If scaling down a full-sized prototype but to metric dimensions it is **far** easier (and safer) to use a decimal scale -1/10 instead of 1/12. This cannot be done for locos which must run on an imperial track, of course, but for other model work there are very considerable advantages.

I need not add that in all cases it is vital to check and double-check your conversion drawings. I might add that such checks may often reveal some errors in the original drawings **before** conversion.

Appendix 1

The Theory of Orthographic Projection

The fundamental theory is rooted in the principles of solid geometry and need not concern us. The basic idea, so far as drawing is concerned, is that there are three planes mutually at right angles, like the sides of a box. The views are projected onto these planes which are then developed or opened out into a flat sheet - the paper we draw on.

In **first angle projection, Fig. 89**, the object with faces A, B and C visible, is imagined to be suspended inside such a box. Three of the sides are shown, one on each of the three planes OX, OY and OZ. The object is viewed in three directions at right angles - I have shown a sketched eye and an arrow to indicate these directions of view. The image behind the object is then drawn on the plane *behind* it; the projection lines from object to plane run in the same direction as the lines of sight. Once all the views have been drawn on the inside of the imaginary box this is cut open and laid flat, as shown at (b). The relative positions of the three views is thus fixed by the projection convention used. The plan lies below the main elevation, and the eye follows the projection lines in that direction. Similarly for all other views. You will see that view of B seen in (b) is exactly what you would see if the object at A had been turned through 90 degrees - the first right angle. For a complete orthographic projection we should use all six sides of the box, producing six views in all. In third angle projection, **Fig. 90**, the object is imagined to be suspended within a transparent box, as shown at (a). The three planes OX, OY and OZ are the same, but the relationship between OY and OZ has changed. Look at the little diagram (c). ZOY forms one right angle - the first, and YOZ' forms another - the second. The third right angle is formed by Z'OY'. The imaginary box is formed round these last two planes, hence the term third angle.

I have again shown sketches of eyes and arrows to show the direction of sight, but this time the image is drawn on the face of the transparent plane, *between* the eye and the object. The line of projection runs *opposite* to the line of sight. Hence you see the face D on Z'OY' - compare with **Fig. 89**.

When the box is opened out we find the views disposed as shown at (b). The plan is now above the main elevation and you can see that to get the face C into that position from the elevation the object must be rotated through *three* right angles. Again, a complete projection would form six views.

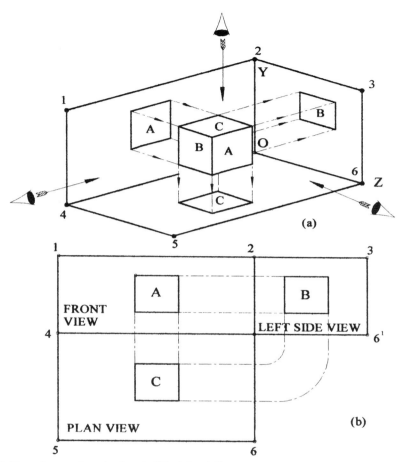

Fig. 89 *The planes of projection in "First Angle".*

Thus both systems are based on a valid conceptual theory. Both, in fact, are based on the same fundamental theories of descriptive geometry of Descartes, Monge and others. In a way, first angle projection is an evolution as the system, or one very similar, was in use long before the theory was propounded, whereas third angle seems to have been developed by American geometricians from scratch very much later. (It was not standardised, even in the US, until 1935.)

First angle is more or less universal in Europe except for some engineering firms with US parents. Third angle is already standard in the US. As already stated, neither is right or wrong but it is *absolutely vital* to be consistent right throughout the works or drawing office, and essential to show on *every* drawing which system is in use. If any deviation from the chosen system is necessary, then direction of view arrows must be used.

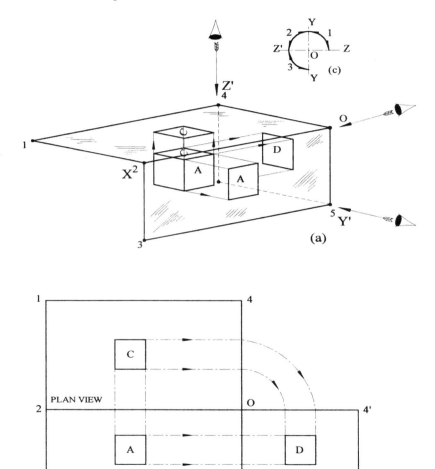

Fig. 90 *The planes of projection in "Third Angle".*

Appendix 2

Standard Sizes of Drawing Paper

Current standard sizes of drawing sheets are based on a sheet which is nominally one square metre in area, each smaller size being one half of the previous one. The sizes are as follows:

A0	841mm x 1189mm
A1	594mm x 841mm
A2	420mm x 594mm
A3	297mm x 420mm
A4	210mm x 297mm

Sizes smaller than A4 are of little use in the drawing office. Drawing-boards are usually about 20 to 30mm larger than the paper size.

The former standard was based on the ancient book paper sizes and were as follows (although variations of up to an inch could be found):

Demy	20 x 15 inches
Medium	22 x 17 inches
Royal	24 x 19 inches
Imperial	30 x 22 inches
Atlas	34 x 26 inches
Double elephant	40 x 27 inches
Antiquarian	52 x 31 inches

A paper known as half imperial, 22 x 16 inches, was much used in schoolwork.

Index